BEAUTIFUL
IN BLACK

BEAUTIFUL IN BLACK

CONVERSATIONS WITH SUICIDE

A True Story

SARA SHAI

BlueSkyChateau

Woodland Hills, CA

Beautiful in Black
Conversations with Suicide
by Sara Shai

Copyright © 2006 by Sara Shai

Shai, Sara.
    Beautiful in black : conversations with suicide : a true story / Sara Shai.
    p. ; cm.

    Includes list of suicide-related resources and discussion guide.
    ISBN-13: 978-0-9785042-0-5
    ISBN-10: 0-9785042-0-8

    1. Shai, Sara. 2. Shai, Moshe. 3. Suicide--Psychological aspects. 4. Suicide
victims--Family relationships. 5. Bereavement--Psychological aspects. 6.
Jewish women--Israel--Biography. 7. Journalists--Israel--Biography. I. Title.

CT1919.P38 S53 2006
956.94/05/092   2006903857

Book cover painting by Sara Shai
Photography by Vern Poore
Cover and Interior Design by Robert Aulicino

Author's note: Several names and places have been changed to protect the
identity of the individuals depicted.

Disclosure: If reading the contents of this book brings up thoughts of suicide
and /or issues regarding the death of a loved one, please call the
National Suicide Preventions Lifeline: 1-800-273-TALK (8255).
For a full list of resources see the Appendix.

Printed in the USA
Published by

BlueSkyChateau
P.O. Box 4307
West Hills, CA 91308
www.BlueSkyChateau.com

This book is dedicated to those who have lost a loved one to suicide And remained silent.

ACKNOWLEDGMENTS

I am deeply grateful to my friend and editor, Susan Ball-Emmerson, for her patience, love and support. Without her this book would not be possible.

I wish to give my thanks to the boarding school Beit-Rivka in Kfar Chabad, Israel for opening their doors to me and my sister at a young age, and giving me the chance to flourish. I wish to acknowledge my brother, Carmel, who always believed in me. His words and actions always empowered me. I want to commend my younger brother, Avi, for his perseverance and kindness, as well as all my nieces and nephews for being beautiful extensions of my dear brothers. To my sister, I send my deepest love and gratitude for standing beside me no matter what challenge I encountered.

I am most indebted to my beloved son for the time I took away from him and can never give back. My love for him and his bright smiles were always the shinning light in my path. To his wife, Yael, and my grandsons, David and Adam, for giving me joy and affection I never knew before.

A thanks to my many friends, especially Mary Hammond and Lynda Du Puis, for being instruments of strength and affection in my life.

I also wish to give my most affectionate salute to the United States of America for its most outstanding constitution for humankind. I love this country and what it stands for.

Most of all I wish to humbly extend my deepest thanks to my Creator for giving me an inner strength and a deep passion to create and sustain the positive life energy that is in me.

CONTENTS

INTRODUCTION

In December of 1970, my husband, Dan Tavor, a noted Israeli journalist, committed suicide. He left many of those who knew him in shock and disbelief. As for myself, I entered a new world of uncertain emotions and confusion as I suddenly became, "the woman whose husband killed himself."

In those days of turmoil and uncertainty, when trust and tranquility were so rare, I found writing to be a most comforting tool. As I wrote, I looked back trying to figure out what had happened and, as time went on, I started to believe that my thoughts and feelings were worth sharing. Especially when life became hard to bear and the effects of suicide were obvious, I would take the book out and start the writing process again.

Soon I would be overwhelmed by my recollections and realize that, in fact, it was far more difficult to bear the influence of its reality than I originally had thought. Then I would put the book aside and hope that I would be able to let go of its contents.

But the truth was that this story kept on demanding my attention and insisted on being told. I felt that I was no longer the one who owned the story, rather that the story owned me.

I noticed day-by-day that something was wrong in my existence. I had adapted to living in this world of guilt and shame and blame. So, no matter how successful I became, I still felt one down and attached myself to the world of "less than."

All the while, I was dragging the effect of suicide along with me. It just would not go away. They say time heals all wounds… well, time was not healing this one.

As my writing progressed, what emerged was a parallel line showing the story of my husband's life, and my own, from our early childhood through our marriage. Hand in hand, two lives—so much alike, yet so diverse. Although I found we had encountered many incidents that were similar, I realized our approach to life was so totally opposite.

Finally, I decided not to resist and actually allowed myself to fully encounter my past and bring the book to completion. There were too many facts that could not be ignored or denied, starting with: suicide is a "silent epidemic." While doing research, I came across some startling information. I learned that, in actuality, the number of suicides in the United States is higher than the number of homicides. Over 31,000 people kill themselves every year in the U.S. alone.

It was time to face these facts head-on. I certainly was not the only suicide survivor and I now felt an obligation to make my story available to others seeking answers.

This created an enormous opportunity not only for myself but, potentially, for many other people as well. It became my intention to use my memoir to shed light on the survivors and their struggles, as well as on the victims of suicide and their constant battle with life and death. It was important to me that their cries for help would finally be heard in a way that could reach more than just the immediate families. Reality, after all, is by far more piercing than any fiction our mind could create.

I have come to this task not as a newly affected person but as someone who has the perspective of more than thirty-five years behind her.

So, come... pull up a comfortable chair and a cup of tea and let me tell you my story.

CHAPTER 1

The Eyes

I would never die for my beliefs because I might be wrong.
— Bertrand Russell

Once he told me, "When I die, you will give me a quiet funeral and walk silently behind my coffin, carrying in your arms a bouquet of white flowers. I love white orchids, but you no doubt will get me gladiolus." He patted me on my back, glancing at me from the corners of his eyes and added, "I really mean it, my love." He did not wait for my answer.

"Nonsense," I said absentmindedly.

But, it seems that he really did mean it!

And so, there I was walking behind his coffin... but not silently, for inside I was furious. I did not carry flowers either. Neither gladiolus nor orchids. I just took off my wedding ring and placed it into a small box in my handbag... for that was Dan's last wish. "Put your wedding ring in my grave. Forgive me for robbing you of it but, after all, I am leaving everything else to you... to you only."

I was late to accompany my husband on his last journey.

I was late for my feet had been reluctant to carry me to the cemetery. The limousine driver had waited for a long time while my family walked around the living room urging me to hurry up. Inside, I felt frozen. I was confused and not sure how it all had happened. I hoped that this was another macabre joke of Dan's or perhaps some kind of a nightmare and I would wake up at any moment.

My grandmother, Sophie, held my hand gently and said, "You should wear black... this red sweater is not appropriate, my child." I noticed her teary eyes and understood now why, yesterday, Dan had asked me to wear the black dress he had bought me in Paris.

There in the morgue he waited for me just as he used to wait when we arranged to meet in town. But this time he was not angry with me for arriving late, or at least, if he was, he could not show it. All were there. His family. My family. His colleagues and associates. His friends and many others whom he had had contact with and even those who knew him by name only. Some journalists who were eager as usual to get some scraps of information had gathered like ravens feeding on carrion to learn why... Why should a young and successful journalist end his life in this manner? Some neighbors and a few curiosity seekers stood in the back and formed a semi circle; some of them had turned their backs to the morgue, facing the cemetery gates and waiting for my arrival.

I entered those gates with my head down. I felt their eyes all over me, narrowing and fixing their gaze directly on me. I felt the weight of this heavy burden bearing down on my shoulders. I stopped in the middle of the circle, lifted my head and dared to look straight back into those eyes. Some of them whispered, some hissed, some yelled noiselessly. They took on a life of their own. They indicted me. They passed judgment without putting me on trial, without giving me the chance to defend myself.

I felt like a warrior facing a lion in an ancient Roman Circus with the savage beast ready to take out my vitals. All around was the crowd, even fiercer than the lion, demanding that the Emperor let me perish between the jaws of the beast.

Later, I could hardly remember who was at the funeral. I just recall the eyes. All sizes and hues. Looking at me, sometimes approaching me and sometimes abandoning me in revulsion. A few hands stretched out to grasp mine, but they were cold and quickly withdrawn even before I felt the handshake that was supposed to express sympathy for the bereaved wife. I stood in place for a long time. My body was numb but my heart was burning with a fury that kept my blood pumping through my veins in a rhythm of rage. Finally, I started to move ahead with uneven, unsteady steps. I saw Dan's younger brother, Gadi, approaching me. He extended his arms with affection.

"They say Dan isn't anymore… that's not true… don't believe them," I cried with pain, jerking my head strongly toward the gathering crowd.

"I know, it is not true… it is not true at all," he said. I felt relief and gratitude for his acknowledgment of me. I threw myself into his arms and savored his embrace. Slowly, he released me and pushed me lightly aside. That was when I heard the piercing yell from Dan's father.

"Go! Go away from here, you murderess!" He moved as if he wanted to strike me but someone held him back.

"Don't listen to him… He is not in his right mind… He doesn't know what he is saying." I heard Gadi's voice as if from afar. I slowly lowered my head recalling what Dan had written in his last letter to me which the policeman had given to me the night before: "And help the old man swallow the bitter pill..."

I saw Barak, Dan's childhood friend, approaching me. He put his arm around my shoulder and I leaned on him in deep appreciation.

What a strange meeting you have arranged for us this time, I said to Dan silently while waiting for his remains to be taken from the morgue. Barak kept supporting me with his strong and solid frame. Dan's body was wrapped in white cloth and was carried on a stretcher by four men. They moved forward and everyone followed them silently escorting Dan to the open grave.

"You know Dan loved you and that's all that matters. Everything else is unimportant. These people are unimportant," Barak whispered to me while moving me along in the funeral procession.

"You mean the eyes, don't you?" I whispered.

"What did you say?" Barak said trying to understand me. He was puzzled and I knew I did not make sense to him.

"Leave me alone. They say I am a murderess... Didn't you hear just now?" I kept on walking forward holding onto his arm in clear desperation.

"You fool," he exclaimed. "Dan knows that is not true," he continued while his eyes searched mine, perhaps wondering if they could get to the core of my truth. Or, was it an attempt to find out the facts?

"Dan knows?" I repeated after him. "So, do you think he can hear me? If he can, I want to talk to him..." Barak had a strange expression on his face and I didn't wait for his answer.

"Will they let me?" I implored.

"Yes, of course, speak. Do whatever you want. After all, it is your life."

I felt an uncontrollable desire to suddenly stand as tall as I could, to place my feet into the ground as deeply as possible. I pulled on my entire life's energy and shouted from the depths of my heart toward the shrouded body longing for the dead to hear me.

"It is not fair… it is not fair at all!" I cried. "You tricked me… you fooled me… you spit in my face… it is not fair that you lied… You told me we could have a new beginning but you did not play fair!" I accused him, blamed him and then charged him again with fury. "It was only yesterday that you said you had tickets to the ballet… I hate you… I hate you… you have lied to me!"

I saw Uncle Abraham rushing to quiet me, asking me to take it easy, but Barak reassured him that it was okay for me to speak. "Let her be… let her be…" he said. My uncle moved to the side but kept following my steps cautiously.

"It is not fair at all," I yelled and my voice began to come out in sobs from my throat. "And, don't tell me you can't hear me… you always had such excellent hearing… listening to three Arab radio stations at the same time… You hear me… you hear me now. You played a dirty trick on me. That's exactly what it is… a cruel, sick, dirty trick!"

I broke into a run as if I wished to exit my body and catch up with the body. Barak followed me with his big steps, trying to contain me. I felt drunk with anger and grief. The eyes continued to stare, continued to watch with shock and disbelief. I slowed down with a feeling of help-lessness. *What is fair about life?* I thought to myself.

People attempted to hush me again. They said some-thing about respect for the dead and regarding the feelings of relatives, as if I was not related to Dan anymore. I refused to be stopped. "I don't care. I want you to hear me, Dan. You invited all these people here… Why?" I sobbed as my voice struggled with my confusion. I turned to Barak and spoke to him quietly. "This is like a large press conference. Why are all these people here… and what about the policemen gathered at our home last night? Why did they come? And, why did they write about Dan in the paper? Dan always said that the press was one big political lie. They distort the facts, is what he said. They exaggerate. Dan exaggerated, Barak, don't you think so?"

I had not expected him to answer but I heard him saying, "You're right, my dear, he did exaggerate." I took a deep breath. It was as if Barak had given me permission to be heard and to be right. I was thankful for that. Looking ahead, I could see that most of the people were in front of us still proceeding after the coffin. We hurried our steps in an effort to catch up. Finally, we reached the open grave and the body was lowered. Psalms were said and the lapel of his father's jacket was torn. This was a Jewish sign of mourning, the symbol of a tear that could not be mended.

The undertaker began to cover the body with earth. "From earth we come and to earth we shall return." Then I recalled Dan's last wish and with shaking fingers I pulled out the little jewelry box from my handbag where I had placed my wedding ring. I lowered my body onto the ground and leaned into the open grave.

"Take it… Do you hear me? Just put out your hand and take it. You asked for it so just take it," I cried. The undertaker moved over to me and took the little box and placed it next to the inert body in the grave. The ghost of a smile played along his thin lips as he continued to shovel

the earth over Dan's body until I could not see him anymore. Barak moved forward and helped me to my feet.

"Is that all? No more Dan Tavor?" I heard his bereaved
father yelling with vehemence. "I want to lie here near my
son, near my Dan! I shall not move from here ever!" he
sobbed. He stretched himself along the grave and threw
earth over his clothes. Dan's younger brother came over to
him and said, "Get up. Get up! I have to say the Kaddish."
He extended his hand and helped the old man to his feet.
Then, he began to read. Occasionally, his voice failed as the
tears choked him. He made an effort to stand tall and pro-
nounce every word with strength and hope. He ended
with a loud lament and all of us looked on in silence.

The burial ceremony came to an end but I remained
standing still as did many others. It was as if we were strangely waiting for an encore. Some murmured in an undertone,
"What a tragedy." Some looked on with blank expressions
on their faces. Some still hoped to get more information to
nourish their need for gossip. And still others watched over
me lest I say or do something inappropriate.

And yet, what was there to say? I was only 24 years old
and already a widow, an abandoned wife. I was not sure
whether I cared more about mourning my loss or defending myself against the judgmental eyes.

Slowly, I kneeled and passed my hand over the fresh,
humid earth. I was yearning now to feel the warmth of
Dan's body as I had never yearned before. I rested my
cheek on the pile of dirt and whispered, "It is not fair. You
have not only killed yourself but also those that you said
you loved most. I am angry with you—really angry."
Unconsciously, I extended my thumb at the grave in a
childish gesture symbolizing I was cross with him.

Then, I felt Barak's hand on my shoulder. I turned around and looked up. His face was pale and full of sorrow. As he extended his arm forward to support me, I stood up next to him. "Let's go," he said. We had taken only a few steps when he stopped short, looked directly into my eyes and asked, "How long did you know Dan?"

"Eight years," I replied wondering about his question.

"So, you gave him an extra eight years of life," he said thoughtfully and walked me out of the cemetery.

CHAPTER 2

The Shiva

The time to pray is not when we are in a tight spot but just as
soon as we get out of it.
—Josh Billings

The following morning I felt fatigued and emotionally drained. Something proud in me had been destroyed and
smashed. It was as if I had been slapped in the face and the
sound was deafening. As if I had been kicked out of life
itself and landed nowhere. In disbelief and agony I buried
my face in my pillow. I wanted to hide and somehow con-
ceal the past. Restlessly, I tossed and turned seeking to find
a way to shake off my nightmare. I wanted to run away
from reality but Dan's suicide kept emerging stronger and
clearer than any dream.

Last night after the funeral, I had been brought to my
grandmother's home in northern Tel Aviv. Everyone was
there, talking, whispering and trying to make sense of what
had just happened to our family. I curled into my grandma's bed and reached for a pillow, almost afraid to let go. As

I struggled with my own inner turmoil of fear, anger and shock, I tried to shut my eyes and sleep, but every sound or movement brought me back to full alert and the reality of the past twenty-four hours.

In the morning the shock rolled over me again. Only a few days ago Dan had been with us and now he was buried and gone forever. It was a cloudy Wednesday outside—just an ordinary day for most people. Just another day on the calendar. Business as usual, but not for me. It felt like it would never be business as usual for me ever again. Yesterday, the soil had been moist, dark, heavy and final. Everything about yesterday had felt final and I could not deny or escape it as hard as I tried. It felt all too vivid and real.

The house was slowly filling up with relatives and friends trying to help. My Aunt Doris walked into the room trying to get me out of bed. She had brought in a cup of tea that she left on the bedside table. She leaned over me and quietly asked me to compose myself. "In respect for Dan you need to get up and look good to greet the guests. This is his Shiva. People are already talking and asking questions, and it is your responsibility to acknowledge them. The rabbi is due at your house any moment now. You've got to get up. This is your life now, poor girl—your fate has been stained. What a tragedy." She sent an uncertain look toward me and took a deep breath.

As she was speaking, my mother stalked into the room and glared at me. "God help you, Sara. What did you do to him?" Her words cut the air sharply. My aunt stood breathlessly waiting for my reaction. Slowly, I sat up in bed. I felt isolated and cold and found I could not speak. It felt as if I had been hit hard. If my own mother blamed me without a question asked, what could I expect from strangers? What could I possibly say in my own defense? A deadly silence permeated the room. My aunt started making her way toward the door; still my mom continued aiming her comments at Doris. "It was probably something between them." With a helpless voice she added, "What are we going to say to people?" She shook her head with sorrow and followed her sister through the door.

How about the truth, I thought. But whose truth, Dan's or mine? Everyone out there seemed to have their own version of the truth, their own adaptation of what might have happened to us. *It's probably best to not utter a word*, I thought. Silence is golden. Wasn't that the old adage?

Like yesterday, it seemed to me as if Dan had exited squeaky clean, and I was now being held accountable for his death. He killed himself and, in return, I inherited the mark of Cain upon my forehead. How I wanted to shut everything and everyone out!

But, no. It was his Shiva, seven days of mourning for the dead. And, I had my responsibilities. Dan's father refused to sit in the same room with me. He had claimed, "I do not mingle with a murderer. I shall honor Dan in my own home." But there were others and I knew I would have to meet with them. Slowly, I got up and began to move around the room.

And so, my family and I observed the tradition of sitting Shiva in Dan's and my house. When I got home, I noticed that the area rug in our living room had been taken away. "We found the rug neatly folded and pushed aside," I overheard Uncle Abraham whispering while rearranging the room for the Shiva.

"I suppose he cared for it and did not want to stain it with his blood," my Aunt Doris added. "It's a good rug.

After all, it is hand woven and of high quality."

The chairs were arranged in a half circle facing our sofa, and Dan's favorite armchair had been moved to the far corner. Our living room furniture was light Danish. It was a clean and simple line of oak wood mixed with black leather. Dan had chosen it only six months ago. Now it all seemed very irrelevant, but six months ago it had been very important and Dan had paid the utmost attention to the style and color of the leather. He did not ask for my opinion and I did not offer it. Personally, I had never liked the Danish style of furniture. To me it seemed to have no imagination. If I had been asked for my choice, I would have looked for something more traditional with woodcarving or maybe some kind of reproduction of an old French style. As for the sofa cover, I would have preferred a bright color in tapestry or deep velvet. Leather would not have been my choice. But I had not been asked and when I was, it was only after it had been delivered and set up in the living room.

"What do you think?" Dan had asked rhetorically.

"It's nice, very modern… it's the 'in' thing," I replied noncommittally. "I'll love it," I lied successfully.

"Sure you will. After all, I chose it," he laughed, throwing his body into the armchair and enjoying its comfort. "You should try this. It feels so good." Later on, smoothing my palms on the soft leather, I discovered that it did.

Now, as I looked around the room, I thought, *If this furniture could only talk—the stories it could tell.* I moved my eyes around the room as people were taking their seats. The rabbi had just entered and sent a quick look toward me. He walked slowly across the room and lowered himself into Dan's armchair. Now that he had arrived, my Uncle

Abraham handed prayer books to the men in the room and they stood up for Kaddish. The rabbi looked around counting the men in the room for a minyan. Jewish tradition requires ten men for the formal reading of prayers for the dead and although there were many women in the room, they did not count.

The men stood up facing east toward Jerusalem and started reciting the Kaddish. Slowly, the women in the room moved toward the kitchen where they listened with respect and quietly set up plates of food.

Mostly, the Kaddish is a prayer of glorification and praise for God. "We are being asked to praise and glorify God NOW," the rabbi explained at the end of the prayer emphasizing the word *now*, "because we are remaining NOW, even while our loved one is gone. NOW more than any other time it is clear that life and death are in the hands of God, and Now, more than any other time, we are asked to honor life."

Some of the people were looking at each other puzzled. Some were quietly shaking their heads in disbelief. After all, Dan had taken his life with his own hands. Was God involved in Dan's death, too? The question was not asked aloud. To this day, I am not sure if the rabbi was ever told about the means of Dan's death. Quiet and a sense of denial followed the rabbi's words. No one dared to doubt him and no one wanted to admit that Dan had, in fact, performed the most forbidden act. The cause of death on his death certificate had been left blank to protect his honor and his family's image. I don't know who was behind it or how it was done. I just know it was done to spare his reputation.

During the seven days of mourning the Jewish tradition instructs many rituals, prayers, and rabbinical commentary.

Anecdotes and biblical stories about life and death are to be told. Conversations are to be loving and reminiscent of the dead. Relatives and friends are encouraged to visit and console the mourners and to relieve them of all responsibilities by running errands and providing meals. It is believed to be a good deed to comfort the mourners, and to help with the grieving process.

The Shiva for Dan was quite different in its nature. The mood was one of shock and disbelief, blame and guilt, curiosity and a desire to know more. The Jewish religion forbids sitting Shiva for a suicide, and even Dan in his final note to me wrote, "You don't have to sit Shiva for me. I hated it in other families, and even the Torah forbids mourning for me." But with no questions asked, totally ignoring his wish and the Jewish law for that matter, we sat Shiva! It was as if we all silently agreed to deny his act and to forgive him. I sat quietly, feeling numb and swallowing the scandal.

My sense of rejection was deep and I felt as though he literally had slammed the door in my face. He left me with no more chances for dialogue, no more give and take and, as the days wore on, my guilt was unrelenting. Day after day I put myself on trial reviewing the events of my life with Dan. I kept searching my soul knowing I had somehow hurt him. The feeling of loss and relief was mixed with the drive to survive. I did not know what would lie ahead but I knew no matter what I would be up and running again to try and make life work.

In public, I kept my head up. I acted by my own laws and instincts, greeting visitors and smiling at people, numbly nodding my head in agreement. I would see their faces and hear their voices but rarely reacted internally. Some of the things I heard were painful but I rarely defended myself. What was the use? Many of our friends slowly but surely vanished, and in time I was left alone. In private, I cried for hours and as time passed I found that I was crying for my life and myself... not Dan's life. He had completed his life and exited with "honor and respect" as he always did. How often I remembered him saying that one has to know when to exit! One has to be remembered at his best.

As one newspaper wrote after Dan's death:

"Dan Tavor, a noted Israeli journalist and commentator, became a victim to the Middle East way of life and his role as a husband... He was in a constant philosophical struggle with life and death."

Dan's mark was recorded in history. As for me, I could not seem to wipe the slate clean. My guilt as "the wife" ran deep in my gut and the circumstances surrounding Dan's death and burial only contributed to my emotional upheaval.

I became a widow at such a young age. I had always pictured a widow to be an old woman, and it was only with deep pain and disappointment that I was able to accept my new title. It was not in my plans at all, not what I had wished for my husband and myself. As the days passed, I felt myself wearing a shroud of sadness and regret. Although in Israel young widows are more common than elsewhere because of the ongoing wars with our neighbors, it was still difficult because of the kind of widow I became. I realized very quickly that there are all kinds of widows and people judge you according to those circumstances.

A woman who loses her husband in the war while he is defending his homeland is specially honored, because by her loss she contributes to the security of her nation. This is a highly honorable place to be in. She receives the compassion and acknowledgment of everyone. A woman who loses her spouse because of an illness also earns the compassion and understanding of her family and friends.

On the other hand, a woman who loses her husband to suicide is a woman who maybe took part in the mistreating and misunderstanding of her man. It is frequently assumed that she had somehow contributed to the deadly act. Just like that. No questions asked. I did not see compassion and understanding in people's eyes toward me. I was damaged goods and try as they might, very few were able to get beyond this reality.

There is an interesting discussion in the Talmud. Jews have a custom of slitting their garments, tearing their clothes to symbolize the ripping apart that death brings. Dan's father had done it at the funeral. The question is asked as to whether, after the period of mourning, can you repair the garment to be used again? The answer by the rabbis is, "Yes, but when you mend it, you should not fold the edges of the fabric under so it will not look as if it has never been torn. It should look mended." This symbolizes the fact that life after death is never the same as before. The next question is, "Can you sell the garment?" The answer is "no" because our life events and experiences are our own and others cannot adopt it.

And so, like the story in the Talmud, I kept on wearing the torn life sentence that Dan had knowingly chosen for me. Even though he knew that his action was forbidden and that we both would be marked by his suicide, he had gone ahead and followed his plan. His action was calculated to the utmost detail and he and I would have to survive that truth.

As the police sergeant handed me the letter that Dan had left for me, he shook his head and said, "I am sorry for your loss, Mrs. Tavor, but it seems like your husband planned his death as perfectly as a military operation." I wondered, *If his death had been the perfect military operation, who was the enemy?*

Time would tell. As my life unfolded, I would, in fact, encounter some of Dan's enemies: his emotions that created controversy and turmoil in his mind from his early life, uninvited feelings and events that developed and soon became a permanent guest in his psyche. I sometimes wondered if Dan's self-inflicted death was in fact his choice, or perhaps he had been a victim in the hands of those "enemies."

As for myself, and the role I played in Dan's life, I believe that at first I was a welcome addition, a friend and a hope to beautify the ugliness. I became a possibility for him to make a difference in his existence, a puppet or scarecrow to chase away the enemies. This was a task I knew nothing about, an honest plot led by Dan's good intention to win his battle with life. While he escaped, however, in one swift gunshot, I took on his unfinished business with life and added it to my own already cluttered burden. We each had our family histories. We each had our strengths and weaknesses. And, ultimately, we each had our own path to walk.

CHAPTER 3

Myself

Honor does not have to be defended.
—Robert J. Sawyer

My stepmother, Celina, was a woman in her forties, with round hips, thin legs and full arms. Her face was mostly red and tight with thin eyebrows framing her eyes. On her forearms she used to wear many pure gold bracelets. They were a substitute bank account for her because whenever she succeeded in putting away a sum of money over fifty pounds, she would run to Ovadia's, the goldsmith shop and order another golden bracelet, its width depending on the sum she could afford to buy. Whenever she became excited or angry she used to shake her hands and the noise those bracelets made served as a cacophonous background accompaniment to her yells.

My Dad had married Celina after his divorce to my mother was in effect. It all happened very quickly. One day, we were a family with a mother and a father and the next day, everything fell apart. My mother and her lover took off and left my father and us behind. The divorce was issued right away and there were no questions asked. It was decided that my mother was not fit to be a parent and so my father was given sole custody. I was the first-born and had just turned twelve years of age. My sister Rechel was only three years younger; my brother, Carmel, was six years old; and, my baby brother, Avi, was only three.

People were astonished. "What kind of a mother would do such a thing?!" "What a selfish bitch!" "The poor children—and the father is such a good man." "She is a disgrace to all mothers!"

I heard all of it and I was determined to take care of my father and my family. At first, I rushed to clean our home—especially the kitchen sink that had been left with piles of dishes and pots still smelling of leftover food that had gone bad. The smell of rotten food was so sharp that to this day it brings back vivid memories of that kitchen in Ramleh. Cigarette butts were everywhere and the floor was covered with layers of dust and dirt. It had only been a few days since my mother had left but our home felt as if it had been abandoned for years.

I rearranged the furniture, washed the clothes, walked my siblings to school and carried my little brother to the nursery across from our development. Then, I ran to attend my own school where I was in the seventh grade.

As time went on, I began to detest going to school. It was a great trial for me. Kids started to point their fingers and whisper among themselves about the tragedy of my family. I eventually became an outcast and no one wanted to be my friend. Later on, I learned that some parents deliberately forbade their children to play with me. On the way to school and sometimes during the break, kids would run around me and shout in my ear, "Your mom is a slut! Your mom is a slut!" I knew where they had heard the words and their mocking laughter was deafening. In order to survive, I learned to shut off my feelings and mind my own business. I had much more important things to take care of, like my brothers and sister.

My father worked nights at the bakery and early one morning, he returned with a grocery bag in his hand. I welcomed the food and started to put it away. I noticed my father's eyes following me and eventually he asked, "Where are your brothers?"

"Playing outside," I replied.

"Go, get them. I have something to tell all of you."

I immediately stopped what I was doing and ran to gather my brothers and sister.

"Come on. Dad wants to talk to us," I entreated. "I think it is important."

We all entered the apartment with some hesitation. There had been too many important events taking place in our lives during the past few weeks and none of them had been good.

My Dad sat at the center of the sofa in the living room. As we entered, he gathered my brothers closer with his arms and motioned for us girls to sit near him as well. I sat on the chair across from them, and my sister, Rechel, fixed herself in the corner of the room. The four of us waited in silence not sure what was coming next. My father smiled, trying to put us in an easy mood, but we were too worried and his smile fell flat. He then took a deep breath and started talking.

"You all know I work nights, every night. I work very hard."

"Yes, we know," I said impatiently.

"So, when I go to work at night, you all stay here alone. This is not good."

"We don't care. It's okay with us," I rushed to speak for everyone. I had an inner notion of what he was preparing us for. I recalled that my Grandmother Lulu, my father's mother, had been visiting us just yesterday.

"Yes, but it is not good for you," he repeated firmly observing each one of us carefully with his eyes. "It is not good for you and it is not good for me," he continued. "I need a wife and you need a mother." He stopped for a few short moments to let his words sink in.

"We don't need a new mother. Sara is helping and cleaning," my brother, Carmel, rushed to explain. He got up from the sofa and stood next to me across from his father. "Won't you continue to clean and cook for us, Sara?" he asked.

I nodded my head strongly. "Dad," I pleaded, "I can do everything. Really I can." My voice was filled with confidence.

"You are still very young and you do not understand," he said with a smile on his face again. "I need a wife, a woman!" There was silence in the room as he continued. "Besides, I have to protect the honor of the family! Things have to get back to normal! My mother will be here again tomorrow and she will take care of everything." He stood up, ending the conversation.

My Grandmother Lulu had never liked my mother. In fact, the two women in my father's life rarely spoke to one another and almost never saw eye to eye. It was only on special family gatherings that they interacted with each other at all.

"I knew it all along. She was not the girl for you," I

heard my grandma saying to my father the next day. "It is all for the best. This divorce is a blessing. It was going to happen sooner or later," she concluded. "I will find you a good woman to take her place."

My Dad kept quiet allowing her to speak her mind and perhaps thinking that maybe she had been right all along.

"And, as for your kids, they need a strong hand. Your wife was not a good mother. Even the court did not find her to be a good mother, so what does that tell you?" She did not wait for an answer.

"They are good kids," my father murmured with a low and careful voice.

"They will be okay," she said absentmindedly. "Kids grow up and forget everything." Walking closer to him, she put her hand on his right shoulder and said, "Listen to me. What you have to think about now is yourself. You have to find a woman to start a fresh new life."

"I understand," he said slowly.

"I am going to the matchmaker this afternoon," my Grandma Lulu replied with a well-satisfied look on her face. She was determined to find a woman for my father. In fact, any woman would do. After all, who would take a man with four kids? It is not such an easy job. Even though everyone knew that my father was a good man and handsome as well, still four kids is a great burden. But, Grandma Lulu was ready for the task.

The matchmaker immediately thought of Celina. She was a strong and healthy woman in her late thirties. She had been married before and had one daughter, a cute nine-year-old. Celina was very emotional and angry at times but that was because she had never gotten over her first husband's verbal and physical abuse.

"He used to beat her up every day," the matchmaker explained to my grandmother. "The divorce was not her fault. Celina is a good and hardworking woman. She is the perfect match for your son. With love and understanding all things are possible," he added, looking my grandmother right in the eyes.

"He will be a good husband for her. As for the kids…" she paused. "Kids need a strong hand. After all, look at their mother and how weak she was."

There were no further questions asked. It was decided. They could not find a better match.

Celina was not kind to us at all. Her demands and rules exceeded a reasonable mind, but we learned to cope and life went on.

June 1959 was when I graduated from elementary school. I was full of lofty dreams and looked forward to doing something important with my life. I really didn't have a clue what I could do, but Celina seemed to have a clear picture for me. One night after dinner, looking back and forth between my father and me, she declared in her thick voice, "Look, Sara, I have a plan for you. School is over and you are now a big girl. I have found work for you at the box factory. You will make 200 pounds a month out of which you will pay us 180 for your keep. The rest will be for fares and pocket money. That should be quite enough," she emphatically concluded. She darted a sideways look at my father and then back to me adding, "You will start work tomorrow. You will go there with Simcha, the carpenter's daughter, who also begins tomorrow."

"I am not going to work in the box factory," I retorted weakly looking at my father and hoping for some sign of support.

Instead, I heard him asking me, "Why?" I was astonished by his question because I remembered my father always praising learned people, always speaking with admiration of those that held good positions in society.

I took my time to answer his question and, when I finally spoke, I could not hide my anger. "I don't believe you. I want to continue with my education and you ask 'Why?' Why?" Trembling where I stood, in clear frustration, I declared, "I want to become somebody!" I choked on my tears.

"Somebody... Who do you think you are, Rothschild's daughter? We are simple people here," Celina exploded. "No big dreams will do here. You are going to work and help your father put bread on the table."

"You... you, shut up! I am talking to my father," I railed back.

"What did she say?" Celina demanded of her husband. "What did she say?"

"Nothing. Nothing at all," he mumbled. Oh, how he hated confrontations. My father's reaction made me furious. I was tired of his fear and submission to Celina and I guess I wanted to show him some bravery.

"I did say something," I yelled. "I just don't want to be here anymore and I don't want to work at the box factory. Boxes remind me of the lowliness of this house."

"So what do you want to do?" my father quietly asked, trying to understand.

"I want to continue my education. You always told me how important it is to learn," I piped up, looking straight into his eyes. He was silent. He closed his eyes and held his head with both hands as if he was searching for an answer. But before he could come up with anything substantial, Celina interrupted.

"What do you want to learn for? Ha, learn what?" she simpered bursting into a laugh. "Stupid kids don't learn. Did you see your report card? Not one 'A.' Not one single 'A.' So what do you have to say about that?" She waited for my reply and, when she sensed my hesitation, she continued, "You are stupid and ugly, and you know it!"

I remember looking at her silently. Not agreeing with her but deep down wondering about what she had said because I had been told that I was stupid and ugly so many times. But I did not feel stupid. I did feel less than everyone else. That was my struggle and it would continue to be my struggle for many years to come. The only weapon I had at this young age was to resist and to prove them wrong. Yet, I did not know how to defend myself now with Celina continuing to challenge me.

"You are stupid and you don't deserve to learn," she spat out and then continued, "Why would you want to learn anyway?"

It was hard for me to hear her attacking voice. True, my report card was nothing to be proud of. I was not a good student at all. My head was too busy with my own thoughts. Like, *Why had my mother left us? Did she ever really love us? Was my father going to be able to take care of us? What was going to happen to my brothers and sister? How could I help them?*

Mostly, I used to sit in the last row in the classroom daydreaming. I don't think I had any particular dream or vision in mind. Anything was better than facing reality. Usually, I hoped the teacher would not call on me and I tried very hard to be invisible. I wasn't a popular student either. I hardly had any friends at school and was not part of any group. At recess time I used to watch the kids play and wished to be part of them but I always felt different. Once, I remember asking one of the popular girls in my class if we could be friends. "Why would I want to be your friend? You're lazy and dull!" Cringing, I saw her rush to tell the 'news' to the rest of the class.

Still I could not agree with Celina calling me stupid! I felt the feelings building up inside of me: the warm almost hot anger in my stomach, the tight, embarrassed sensation in my throat, the unbearable shame. It was too much to take in. I told myself that I would one day prove her wrong. Maybe not today, maybe not right now, but one day I would show her the real Sara. In my mind's eye I could see myself growing out of my deprived village and moving into the vast world outside. Someday, I could see me being free to be all that I could be. Someday, I would stand tall and proud and I would be smiling then. My father would look at me with that special pride I so longed for and he would see for himself that I had been right all along to continue my education. Deep in my heart I believed he was on my side. Deep down in my soul I knew he wanted to back me up and send me to school. How could he not? He always had told me to keep studying and excel. He always had praised those who did. And yet now, he sat there silently. How could he not rescue me from Celina's bitter hatred?

Her voice echoed in my head and yanked me back into the present. "And why would you want to learn anyway?"

"Maybe to learn how to get bracelets like yours," I shouted straight into her face. I don't know where I found the courage to talk to her so. Was I envious of her bracelets? Was I envious of her relationship with my father? My younger brothers and sister stared at me with astonishment for daring to speak back to her in this manner. Her authority was well rooted already in our home and no one spoke back to Celina, not even my own father.

Celina looked puzzled. "You are never going to get bracelets, that's for sure, baby. These bracelets are not the result of a college degree," she said breaking into a loud guffaw and twisting her face into the most hideous grimace. She dropped her body into the armchair nearby and jiggled her bracelets in front of my face.

All this time my father sat dumbfounded. He looked at me meditatively, his forehead wrinkled as if he was in deep thought. I hoped I had sparked in him some identification with my wishes. After a long silence he said, "In order to learn you're going to need money." He nodded his head and concluded, "I don't have any money. I can't give you anything. The money I make is hardly enough to pay for our food." He extended both his hands to me, palms up, and pointed to the rough spots from his heavy tools. "Look, I do not earn my daily bread easily. I thought you could help me. I thought you could help your family." He lowered his head looking at the floor silently.

I felt sorry for my father but I still could not go to work at the box factory. My desire to rise above was stronger. I did not want to end up like my father or my stepmother. I wanted more for myself. "I can't go to work and help you, Dad. I want to continue my schooling," I said with tears in my eyes.

At this, my stepmother's mocking smile changed to an open leer. She said harshly to my father, "She wants to ruin you just like her mother." Celina got up from her chair and glared down at my father. "You are raising a snake on your chest! Sure she wants to learn, but she will not help you one little bit… Far from it. If you think these children will ever help you, you must be dreaming." She looked at my brothers and sister who had been sitting silently all along, and then turned toward me with determination in her voice. "You begin work tomorrow!" And with that she left the room and disappeared into the kitchen.

My father and I stared at each other silently. I tried to repress the grief that welled up inside me and with much courage I whispered, "I shall not work tomorrow! I need some fare money from you. Tomorrow, I am going to look for a boarding school or a kibbutz... I don't want to be here any longer."

Our home was a very small apartment. One could not speak or do anything without being noticed or heard. I knew that my stepmother, even though she was in the kitchen, could hear every word I said. But that did not stop me.

"So, you have decided all by yourself... you are really going to leave me! It is your way or no way!" I could see the disappointment in his eyes.

"Dad, it is not that. You see..." I stammered trying to explain. But he got up and turned toward the bedroom muttering to himself in anger. I followed him and stood in the doorway. "I am not leaving you."

"Oh, no? Maybe Celina is right. Maybe you don't care for me." In a flash Celina was behind me, pushing me out of the way and supporting Dad's fear.

"I told you that she doesn't care... she is a selfish bitch, just like her mother!" She joined my father in the bedroom and shut the door in my face.

I stayed frozen in place for a long moment and then turned around and faced my brothers and sister. They lowered their heads down, sorry for my defeat, and it was easy

to feel their sadness. They moved slowly toward our bedroom. In our room there were two single beds. My sister
and I slept on one and my two brothers shared the other.
During the rest of the evening nobody brought up the
topic about my desire to continue schooling. My siblings
went to bed accepting the verdict and feeling sorry for me.

CHAPTER 4

The Plan

Only the educated are free.
—Epictetus

Before getting into bed, however, I made my plans. I took out the booklet we had received at the end of the school year in which were listed the names of all the high schools in the Tel Aviv region as well as some boarding schools and kibbutzim. I carefully folded it and thrust it into my trouser pocket. In order not to arouse suspicion, I flattened the bulge it made. Then I turned off the light and got into bed next to my sister. At that moment I heard Celina yelling from their bedroom. "I prepared sandwiches for you. You've got to get up at five o'clock sharp tomorrow morning. Simcha will be waiting for you at the bus station." I tucked myself under the blanket and pulled the covers over my head.

But I did not sleep that night. I realized that the fare to the factory would not be sufficient to visit all the schools. I had to have more money. The room was dark.

Only a few cool rays from the full moon entered through the shutters. The sound of the clock ticking and the deep breathing of my siblings kept me company. Now and then, my sister tossed and turned next to me but I lay there feeling calm because I had a plan. Nothing was going to stop me.

Sometime after midnight, I got up very carefully though trembling with fear. I tried to find my way in the darkness hoping not to fall on something and awaken my sleeping family. With the utmost care, I made my way to the bathroom and opened the door praying it would not creak. Fumbling around in the dark, I felt for my father's trousers and slid my hand nimbly into his pocket. I held my breath as I heard the sound of small change. Knowing that my stepmother was particularly sensitive to the tinkle of coins, I moved ever so slowly and inched seven coins out of his pocket, carefully wrapping them in toilet paper. Holding my breath, I returned to my bed and tucked myself in with my small package. When I heard my stepmother's heavy snoring in the next room, I breathed a sigh of relief and smiled to myself.

At five o'clock sharp I felt Celina's hand pulling off my covers. "Get up. It's time," she muttered as she walked toward the kitchen to fix breakfast. We ate in silence that was finally broken by her saying, "Here are two sandwiches and some money. Don't lose it. And make sure you work hard, or they'll fire you. Underneath it all, I think you try to be a good girl." She wrapped the sandwiches with newspaper and handed them to me. Meanwhile, I sat on the edge of the chair not saying a word.

At the bus station Simcha waited for me. She met me with a wide smile. "It's going to be wonderful," she eagerly told me. "My parents promised to buy me two dresses from my first paycheck."

Her words put an ache in my heart. "My parents..." she had said. Since my parents had gotten divorced, I used to imagine that everyone else had the same problems as we did. When I saw or heard of people who had a "complete" family with a mother and father who met every evening at the dinner table, and did things together, it used to sound almost unreal. I had tried to tell myself that broken families were what happened to everyone and in fact, it was the normal order of things that happened in life. This moment when Simcha said that her parents had promised her a dress was one of those moments of unreality for me. I used to go to that place where reality and fantasy switched back and forth. It was with a lurch in my heart that I realized my fantasy world was not the real one, and that some children did, in fact, have that wonderful world with two loving parents. The pain hurt deeply but I had no time to deal with it right then. I pushed it away and started telling Simcha about my plan. I went straight to the point, knowing the bus would be here at any moment.

"Look, Simcha, I want to tell you something." The serious expression on my face got her attention immediately.

"What is it?" she asked eagerly.

"You first have to swear to me that you won't tell anyone."

" I swear," she whispered raising her hand in a solemn oath.

"I am not going with you to the box factory!" I burst out. She looked at me with utter astonishment and, not waiting for her to respond, I continued, "I don't want to work. I want to find a boarding school for myself." I pulled the school booklet from my pocket and straightened the pages. "Look, I have a list of schools… one of them will take me. What do you think?" I examined her expression waiting for some sign of encouragement. Instead, she had a puzzled look on her face.

"Why would you want to go to a boarding school? We just finished school. You must be crazy. Besides, you really didn't like school so much. Don't you want to earn some money? We don't have to tell our parents how much we're making!" She poked me lightly with her elbow as if she wanted to wake me up. "I want to work and make money. I want to buy things, pretty things like makeup, fancy clothes, and jewelry. And I want to have fun. Maybe even get married."

"I know, Simcha, but I have a different plan. I just want you to help me."

"How?" she queried, eyeing me suspiciously.

"I don't want my stepmother to know. It should be our secret."

"Why? What are you up to?"

"Nothing bad. I want to look for a school, a boarding school, that's all," I replied.

"You will get in trouble with her," she finally said.

"I know."

"You shouldn't do it. Come with me. We'll have fun. It's not hard work at all."

"No," I said moving away from her. "My mind is made up. When you get home tonight from work, just tell Celina that I am working overtime. She'll love it," I said trying to convince myself.

"Aren't you afraid?' she asked.

"Not anymore," I murmured.

We stood there for a short moment looking at each other while the bus approached and then Simcha was swallowed into it beaming and glowing with her own excitement. I turned in the opposite direction looking for the central station to take the first bus to Kfar Habonim, the first kibbutz on my list.

At the school's office they did not show much interest in me. The director sized me up with suspicion. "How old are you?" he asked.

"Thirteen years old, sir," I replied timidly.

"Where do you live now?" he continued.

"In Ramleh with my stepmother," I said hoping to evoke some compassion from him.

"And your parents know you are here?"

"Yes!" I lied. "I am looking for a boarding school for myself."

He scratched his head slowly and then insisted that I bring one of my parents with me. I think he thought I was a runaway and he had no more time to listen to my story. He got up from behind his desk and walked me to the door. As I walked away, I saw him looking at my clothes. He could not help but notice my run-down shoes. I understood then that I had not won his sympathy but only his contempt.

Thank God, his was not the only school on my list and I took the bus to the next school. But I was not successful at my next visit either. This time, I tried to hide my torn sandals and gathered together all my positive energy to make a good impression. After two minutes the principal said, "What you need is a haircut and a good night's sleep. Go home and be a good little girl."

At five in the afternoon, I reached the last school on my

list, Kfar Habad, in a small village near Tel Aviv. This was an orthodox boarding school for girls only. An orthodox school was not my first choice but by now I was ready to take any one that would be willing to listen and take me seriously. I got off the bus and looked at the long dusty road leading to the school. On both sides of the road were orange groves, but looking ahead there was no sign of life. Nervously, I started walking, taking long steps and trying to reach the school before dark.

I walked for more than half an hour before I was able to see a few buildings on the horizon. When I reached the first building, I asked for the principal's office and knocked lightly on the door. This time I spoke with confidence looking straight into the rabbi's eyes. It was my last chance and I was determined to get my point across.

To this day I don't know where I drew the courage to do what I did. I began to speak of my dreams. I sat on the chair with self-assurance and told him that I had almost attended another school but that I preferred this school because I wanted to follow in the religious path.

"I've got to find a good school because I know what I want for myself," I told him. I saw him smiling to himself, smoothing his long beard, and nodding with understanding. Still, I was surprised that he did not throw me out of his office. On the contrary, he kept listening and nodding his head in agreement. I think he found my story to be an ambitious one. He did not seem to mind my torn sandals or my messy hair. Finally, he opened his top drawer and handed me an application.

"Please fill in this paper and I will be right back," he said as he stood up and left the room.

I looked at the form, not believing I had gotten through

the first step. With shaking hands I started to fill in the blanks and, suddenly, it washed over me that maybe my dream might be possible.

When the rabbi walked back in, I handed him the application and he promised to help. As for the school fee, he gave me an optimistic smile. "We will try to find a way to get the money through the Office of Social Affairs," he said, picking up a pen and noting something on my application. "We will mail you an answer," he added with self-assurance.

"I am willing to pay you back when I graduate," I replied with enthusiasm.

"That will not be necessary," he said, smiling again.

I felt the ground under my feet strong and solid. I walked out and raised my head, looking at the sky. There was not one cloud. It was clear and open and, as I looked around, all I could see was beauty. I started walking and soon my pace quickened. Bursting into loud laughter, I started running down the dusty road, feeling as if my feet were not touching the ground. Then, abruptly, I stopped. I had to take it all in.

I made my way into the beautiful orange groves and reaching up I picked one of the biggest oranges I could find. As I started peeling and eating the sweet, juicy fruit, I sat down on an old tree trunk. I was so enjoying this moment of triumph, this moment of self-approval. The big juicy bites of orange were as sweet and fresh as life itself. Finally, I stood up again and continued walking, this time a bit slower and starting to come back to my senses. I noticed it was starting to get dark and the first thought of Celina since early that morning entered my mind.

I arrived back home shortly after eight o'clock. As I entered our home with a big grin on my face, I looked at my brothers and sister and knew there was trouble ahead. I was so preoccupied with my gratitude and self-fulfillment, however, that I pulled up a chair and stood up on top of it. Spreading my arms with victory, I said loudly, "I did it! I knew I could. I think I have found a school for me."

Celina walked over to me, her face stony and her hands planted on her wide hips. She shook her head and pulled me roughly off the chair. Holding my chin, she yelled into my face, "You fooled me, you liar, you little bitch. You are a liar and a thief. I know everything you did and you are going nowhere! You will be locked in the bathroom tonight. All night. Do you hear me, you little bitch?"

She pushed me toward the bathroom and I did not resist. I allowed her to have her way. After all, I had had mine. She locked the door and turned the key twice. But, Celina could not spoil my joy that night. In fact, that night was a turning point for me. I learned the biggest and most wonderful lesson of my young life: "If I think I can, I can."

In the days following my success I lived in constant tension and quarrels with my stepmother. My father hardly interfered and many times did not even know what was going on under his own roof. His work as a baker kept him frequently away from home during the night. His workday would end in early morning and Celina would make sure he would get his eight hours of sleep from morning until late afternoon. We were not allowed to speak to him or disturb his rest.

I minded my own business and tried to stay out of the way. My most important focus was the mailman. I waited for midday when the postman would arrive and asked him if he had a letter for me. I told him over and over again how important it was to hand it to me and to me only. I was afraid that Celina would get hold of it and that would put an end to my hopes and dreams. Three weeks went by until I finally received an answer from the orthodox girls' school in Kfar Hadab. It was in the affirmative.

That evening I waited for my father on the street corner on his way to work. He used to ride his bike to save the bus fare and he would always pass by the same way. I knew I would see him and I needed to speak to him privately. It was most important for me to get his permission. I hoped he would even give me his blessing. There was a hope that he would be true to himself, especially now if Celina was not around. Anyway, I needed to be face to face with him without Celina's interruption.

I saw him from a distance walking his bike. It was a good time I thought. He was not in a rush. I knew that he saw me, too. I was looking forward to showing him the letter and sharing my joy with him. As I approached him, I said, "Look, Father. I got the letter of acceptance." I raised the letter closer to his face so he could see it. He continued walking as if he did not hear me. "Father," I demanded, hurrying my steps.

He finally stopped, turned toward me, and said, "Yes. What do you want now?"

"I got the answer. They accepted me. I am going to a boarding school." I handed him the letter, still holding on to its edge, as if afraid it would be taken away from me.

"Are boys there, too?" he asked indignantly.

"No, no just girls," I was happy to say. "It is a religious school. It is a boarding high school and then a teachers' college." I scanned his face anxiously trying to find a ray of acceptance.

"How much is it going to cost and how am I going to

pay for it?" He put down his bike and took the letter out of the envelope.

"They are going to arrange the matter with the Office of Social Affairs. That's what the director told me when I was there," I rushed to answer. "You don't have to pay. You see… you don't have to pay." There was no answer from him. No reaction at all. I continued cautiously. "All I need are two sheets and one blanket. See, it is all written here," and I pointed to the second page. "I have two more weeks before the beginning of the school year." I stared at his face, waiting for him to say something, anything. Slowly, I took the letter from his hands.

"All right, but I can't promise anything. There are still two weeks to go," he said quietly, speaking somewhere in the direction of the space between us.

"I know… I know," I whispered actually quite pleased with his words. This was more than I had expected.

"This is a bad start," he murmured. "Like their mother, all my children will go away and leave me alone."

His last remark came as a sharp blow. My father had never been a decisive man. He always left space for escape. On his face now was a reflection of two different feelings. One was of self-pity, a victim of his circumstances, and the other a feeling of being aloof and standoffish, a feeling of detachment. It seemed to me that he did not consider himself to be a man of courage, although he almost always had the last word in a discussion, even if 'the last word' was only muttered or whispered. It was still always his last word that kept on ringing in midair, always kept me wondering, "What did I do wrong now?" One more time this feeling was so familiar to me and I pushed it to the side with the rest of the jumble of emotions I already was experiencing.

My father picked up his bike lightly, climbed on it and left without another word. As I started walking slowly toward home, I realized he had taken something away from me. I felt empty and drained.

Our apartment was situated in the center of an apartment development inhabited by those who were evacuated from the slums of our town of Ramleh. It was not a much better place than the slum itself. Scattered here and there were sand dunes on which barefooted children played. Washing hung from the balconies, and all around shouts of mothers calling their children mingled with the "juicy" curses of angry fathers. To escape from this pandemonium I used to climb up on a small hill facing our development. There I could look up and see everything in colorful pictures. The shouts then sounded more like the live orchestra of life itself.

After my talk with my father, I made my way to my hill. I sat on the white rock, my favorite one. It was big and smooth and stuck in the ground with its face up. I used to sit on it and caress the cool and flattened surface. I lowered myself down as the sun began to leave the horizon and a dim reddish light covered the sky. I made a silent promise to myself. *When I return here, I will be somebody, somebody my father will be proud to have as a daughter. Then he will see that I never really left him. Then he will see that I really do care and love him. He will see that I am not a bad person. Celina finally will be quiet and humbled once and for all.*

And, as for the fear that I would become like my mother, I was not sure I could see that part clearly yet. True my mother had done an unspeakable thing. She had left her family for another man, an adventurer, a younger man. But, that didn't mean I would follow in her footsteps. I took a deep breath and looked around. I wondered if this hill would still be here in the years ahead to witness my vows.

Coming back to reality was not such fun but it was necessary. I came down from the hill and slowly walked home where I was greeted by Celina's angry face. "So you have come home at last. Where have you been? On the hill playing in the dirt? So that is how you want to learn? That's how you want to become somebody?" She pointed her finger at me sharply and said, "If you go to your boarding school, do not come back. Go and don't come back!" She clapped her hands and the bracelets clanged.

"Oh, yes, I will come back, Celina," I retorted. "I have my brothers and sister and my father here. I will come back!"

"Look at you. You're not even thirteen years old and what a big mouth you have!" she yelled angrily. We glared at each other and I knew it was not over yet.

The next outburst I had with Celina was that Friday night. The Sabbath was the only night my father did not work and it was usually a good evening for all of us. My father would sit at the head of the table. After he blessed the wine and the bread, he would always tell us how lucky we were to have a nice cooked meal and to be living in a free Jewish state. My big brother, Carmel, used to gaze into my father's eyes with admiration and a deep desire to please him. My younger brother, Avi, was only four years old and he always chose to sit near me. My younger sister, Rechel, was helping Celina in the kitchen that night when my father said, "This is Sara's last Sabbath with us." I was surprised that he remembered and found it important enough to note it.

"Yes, the last one," Celina called. "We don't need you

here. You're leaving because you do not care to help your father," she added as she emerged from the kitchen with a big spoon in her hand.

"Enough of that," my father said sharply. "If she wants to learn, let her have her way. Look at me! I, too, wanted to continue my education but my father wanted me to help at the bakery. I did not have my way. Let her at least have hers!" My father's voice seldom reached such a high pitch.

"Oh, yes? Let her have her way? What kind of talk is that? And who will pay? What benefit will you get from it? She is leaving you just like her mother did!"

"I don't want her to curse me one day for not letting her study like I curse my parents every time my work becomes unbearable." He continued speaking very softly, as if he was talking to himself.

"You are too sentimental!" Celina spat back. "You are still going to have to pay money for her studies. How will you pay?" she demanded.

"The Office of Social Affairs will take care of it," he said quietly hoping to ease her off his back.

"And if not? If they will not pay, then what?" she growled.

"Then we shall sell your golden bracelets," I yelled at her.

Her anger nearly choked her. She turned to me with renewed fury. Biting her lower lip, she shouted in my face, "What have you got against my bracelets?"

"They are deafening me with their noise," I cried. "Why don't you sell them and help my father with his burden?"

"They were a gift. You do not sell a gift," she said looking at my father. "Besides, it is none of your business, little girl," and with that she closed the subject.

That night I heard my father and Celina whispering in

their bedroom. "Don't send her to school. There is no use in it at all. She will flunk. She should go to work and help us." Celina was whispering but her voice was still loud enough for me to hear every word.

"I still don't know what I should do," he answered in his usual hesitating way. It made me quiver to hear him and yet, I was not surprised at all. Perhaps he needed to soften Celina up just to get a night of love from her. I heard him whispering how beautiful she was, and kissing her and saying, "Just leave it alone, baby. If it bothers you so much, we will do whatever you wish."

I heard her kissing him back and whispering in her thick, guttural voice, "Sara should work for a few years to help us out. After that we could marry her to a nice boy. But, if you leave her to her own devices, who knows what might become of her. She could become just like her mother." I could hear in her voice that she wanted my father to think she was being caring and loving toward me.

"It is a religious girls' school. There are no boys," he explained gently.

"Still Sara needs to be here working and helping you, helping her family."

There was no answer from my father. I only heard the squeaking of the bed and the sound of their lovemaking. I heard my father moving under the blanket, nesting himself closer to her. He needed her now. His drive to satisfy his sexual need was above all else and I could hear the urgency in his breathing. But Celina couldn't let it go. She was still hammering away. "I just want the best for you, honey," she murmured. "Who knows what kind of a school it is after all."

I felt a deep pain of abandonment that my own father could not stand up. I was alone on my journey to better my life. Could I do it all by myself? Could I do it without my father's blessing?

"We'll think on it," I heard him panting. "We'll wait and see," and with that they sealed my fate with a kiss.

CHAPTER 5

Women Need a Dream, Too

*Nothing has a stronger influence psychologically on their
environment and especially on their children than the
unlived life of the parent.*
—C.G. Jung

But Celina had not sealed my fate and I did go on to
boarding school. The years I spent away from my father's
home were magnificent. In the boarding school, I lived in
a healthy and loving environment. I concentrated on my
studies, took care of my room, and contributed about two
hours a day to the common needs of the boarding school.
Now and then, there were social events and educational lec-
tures. It was a real life in progress and I loved it. I was eager
to learn and become an excellent student. Acquiring knowledge became a source of pleasure and fulfillment for me. I
loved my teachers and admired the school's principal, Rabbi
Dashan, who became a role model in my life. Many years
later, after I graduated, I used to remember his words of wisdom and apply his positive attitude to my everyday life.

Being away from home, I still worried about my brothers and sister, but I did not have to do this on a daily basis. The first year I visited my father and Celina a few times, and it was hard to witness the abuse my brothers and sister had to go through. My arguments with Celina only made life more difficult for them after I left. I carried some guilt about that.

Two years later I finally spoke with Rabbi Dashan and told him what my family was going through. I was especially concerned about my sister, Rechel, who had become Celina's personal maid and scapegoat. She was three years younger than I, but not a fighter at all. She submitted to Celina's demands and her life became more and more difficult. Whenever I saw her, her spirit always seemed to be down. Rabbi Dashan arranged to meet with my father and had Rechel accepted into a special program at our boarding school. It felt so wonderful seeing Rechel during the break time and knowing she was in a safe and healthy environment. It made me feel that I had finally fulfilled a promise I had made to myself before I left home—to watch out for my family.

Being in Kfar Chadad allowed me to be in touch with the inner part of myself and I loved the young woman I was becoming. I was starting to get a lot out of life and I was developing a desire to give back. Even though I was lonely at times, there was a smile on my face now, and a tilt to my head, and great respect for the little Sara inside of me. I felt an innocent aura around me that I had never known before and it felt good knowing that I had done much of this growth on my own. I kept a grateful heart for the Social Affairs Office and their help, but I knew that most of the hard work had been accomplished by me. I had taken the initial action and pursued my dream and for that I felt proud and strong.

Often I remembered what my father had said to Celina, "I don't want Sara to curse me as I curse my parents." I felt compassion for my father, knowing that he lived his inner life feeling sorry for himself. He was unable to take charge and fulfill his desires. In many ways, his life remained barren and unfruitful like a silent symphony or an unfinished song. He lived his entire life holding his parents responsible for his misfortune and blaming his wife and children for leaving him. I could see it written on his face and it caused me sadness deep in my heart.

I knew that my father was a strong force within me, a vitality set deep down inside my soul. His was a love I did not want to lose, an energy I did not want to give up, an approval I craved so very much. My ties with him were unconditional. He was a part of me—his DNA was rooted in my blood. During the early years of my life I remember spending intimate and cozy times with my Dad. They were moments that have always remained with me. To this day I miss them and wish I could recapture them if only for a moment. I especially loved Sabbath morning. He would wake up very early and prepare our breakfast. My Mom would join us later as she loved to sleep in. He would gently kiss her and greet her with a wide smile.

"Good morning, my queen. Sit right here," and he would point to the head of the table. "I am serving breakfast. What do you wish, my lady?"

I used to watch them with an inner joy when things were right between them, and with fear and a breaking heart when things were wrong. From early on, I knew that it was hard to please my mother.

"Just coffee," she would reply, "and don't make such a big deal out of everything. You know I don't like to eat in the morning."

"I know, I know, but the kids love it," he would say while pouring coffee into her mug. "It's a good time for us to be together like this."

I used to stand close to him trying to help while he was serving the food. I loved watching him heat the milk. Fresh milk needed to be boiled and I would watch the foam rise to the top of the pot. My father knew exactly the right moment to remove it from the heat and then he would scoop the foam from the top with a big spoon, looking at me from the corner of his eye, knowing that I would be eagerly waiting for it. He would hand me the spoon carefully and I would lick it with joy. That was my bonus before breakfast. It was the little things like this that warmed my heart.

In the afternoon we would ride his bicycle together. He would put me in front of him hugging my little body with his left arm and holding the bicycle handle with his right. I used to examine his arms, stroking the hair on them gently and grabbing their muscular strength to secure myself. I would always sit with a special pride knowing that I was protected and safe. As we rode through the streets of Ramleh, some people knew him and they would raise their hand in a friendly greeting.

Sometimes, he would point at some of the bulletin boards and test my reading skills. "Can you read this?" he would ask. "You can learn a lot just by reading bulletin boards. There are many of them and it is good practice."

As a little girl, I remember admiring him, thinking he was the most handsome and strong man in the whole world. He was tall with broad shoulders, light olive-colored skin, and deep dark hair. He had a thick mustache that sometimes covered part of his upper lip. At times, when he smiled, there were two dimples on his cheeks. It felt so good to please him and see that smile brighten his face. Although I didn't know it at the time, it was an emotional and spiritual need that went deep into my core. As much as I needed air and water for my body, that was how much I needed his love for my soul.

After his divorce from my mother, I never got to feel his warmth again. He walled himself apart from us and became a mystery I could never unfold. How I longed for a gentle word, a warm embrace. And yet, there was nothing. His smile came very rarely and the dimples seemed to disappear. It had always been my wish to make him proud of me. How I hoped that one day he would come to love me again like before and accept me fully for whom I was. As the years went by, it seemed to be the hardest thing to achieve.

During the five years I spent in the boarding school, my father visited me only once. It is still as vivid and fresh in my mind as if it were today. It was around one thirty on a hot summer afternoon when I heard my girlfriend calling my name. "Sara, you have a visitor. It's your father!" she said with disbelief knowing how much that meant to me.

"My father?" I gasped. It was hard to believe.

"Yes, that's what he said," she replied pointing toward the main road. I followed her to see for myself and saw my father in the distance walking his bike and using his handkerchief as a hat to protect him from the blazing sun. I rushed as fast as I could to greet him, feeling so fortunate for the visit.

"Father, I am so glad to see you," I cried. His face was full of perspiration and I quickly pointed my hand toward the school's building. "Come in and I will show you around. There is a water fountain inside and chairs in the lobby to rest. Come in. Come in." I put my arms around him and urged him forward. He stopped me by raising up his hand.

"I come here only for a few minutes." He put his hand in his pocket and pulled out a letter. "See, I come for this. I need your signature," he said breathing heavily. He pulled the handkerchief off his head and wiped his face. I noticed it was moist and soiled.

"My signature? What for?" I asked, confused, glancing at the letter.

"Your mother is asking money from me. She went to court. Your signature will prove that I am still taking care of you. I don't have extra money for her so you need to sign here for me," and he pointed out the space for my signature. His voice was a bit shaky. I was wondering if he thought I might refuse him. After all, he really did not take care of me at all anymore. Not even money for books. He had made it clear that money was out of the question and I had never asked.

I lowered my head for a moment and then looked straight into his eyes and said, "That's okay, Dad. I will sign, but don't you want to come in first? Maybe rest a little?"

"No, no, just sign here," and he pointed to the last page of the letter restlessly. "I have to go now!"

I took the letter in my hand and he pulled a pen from his shirt pocket and handed it to me. Quietly, I signed. Then he turned his bike around and left. He did not say goodbye. One more time I was left with that uneasy feeling with my father. Was he angry? Did he dislike me? One more time I wondered what I had done wrong?

I could not help blaming myself. I always took it personally. It never dawned on me that my father had his own set of problems that influenced his actions, his own set of beliefs that made him who he was. As a young girl, all I knew was that he had left without saying "good-bye." How was I to comprehend what had just happened? After all, I had done what he wanted me to do. I had signed the paper with no questions asked. I had done what any good daughter would have done and obeyed her father. And yet, why did he leave without a kind word? Was he still angry with me, still believing Celina's harsh words, "She is leaving you just like her mother." Was he now retaliating?

It left me with a deep sense of abandonment, something that I could not get accustomed to. Every time it happened, I had to relive some wrenching feeling of loss. I wanted to clench onto something or someone to feel safe.

My eyes still followed him watching him ride farther and farther down the road until I could not see him anymore. How I wished he would just turn around and come back to wrap his arms around me, or say something like, "It was good seeing you, little girl. Good-bye for now." How I longed for some little tidbit that I could carry back to the boarding school. Something that would carry hope and kindness with it. Something that would show his pride in me and what I was doing with my life. And yet, I knew I was asking the impossible.

I walked back toward my school with slow and heavy steps feeling that one more time something very precious had been taken away from me. Feeling drained and alone, I approached a bench under a nearby tree and sat down.

The tears came then and I cried for my father and I cried for myself. When the tears abated, I slowly got up and walked back to my school.

At eighteen, I graduated from the Hasidic teachers' college 'Beit Rivka' in Kfar Chadad. Graduation night was very special although no one from my family showed up. My Uncle Abraham had promised he would try to be there but, at the last minute, he could not make it. I was still proud of myself, however, and felt very lucky. I had completed the requirements at an early age, and now I was looking forward to my new life of teaching children to be all they could be. Full of ambition and creative ideas, I immediately started teaching in Kiryat-Gat, a small city in the south of Israel.

On weekends I used to take the bus to Tel Aviv and spend time with my Grandmother Sophie. I had gotten in the habit during my years at the boarding school. My mother's side of the family was very understanding and loving toward me. I believe they felt guilty for my mother's actions. Her brother, my Uncle Abraham, refused to talk to her for many years. In fact, he suggested at one point that the family should disown her.

One night when I was visiting them from boarding school, I heard him speaking to his older brother. "She was always hard to control. Her husband was not strong enough to keep her in line, and so, she brought disgrace to the entire family."

"I know. She is ahead of her time," his older brother replied.

"What do you mean? It has nothing to do with 'ahead of her time' or not. She is running around with men. Don't you get it? A married woman with four kids! It is simply wrong and immoral. It is insanity!" Abraham raised his voice in frustration. "We have to stop her, lock her up if we have to! Clearly, she is not in her right mind. She's left a husband and four kids… What does she think she is doing?!" He closed his fist in anger.

"She is only twenty-five years old," my older uncle said on her behalf.

"Who cares how old she is," Abraham continued as if talking to himself. "If only I knew where she was…"

"Ashekelon. She is shacking up with her lover," sneered my Aunt Doris as she walked into the room.

"Who told you?" Abraham inquired.

"Mom," she said quietly.

"Mom?! Is Mom still covering up for her? Why didn't she tell me?" barked Abraham.

"She has always protected her beloved daughter," Doris said with a hint of envy. "She always cared for her more than the rest of us." Doris was Mom's younger sister and had always felt like the least cared for.

"What kind of an example is it for her kids, especially her oldest, Sara?"

I knew that deep down he was also worried that I might follow in my mother's footsteps. He used to keep a close eye on everything I said or did. When he would visit me at school, he would tell me how important it was for a girl to be modest and humble. I knew that he appreciated my studies yet I always sensed his suspicions and concerns about me. Always, I had to carry the burden and deep sense of responsibility about my mother with me.

Once my family's honor and dignity had been stained, it was difficult for me to feel like I belonged anywhere. Yet, with my mother's family I felt that I did belong. I especially felt very close to my grandmother. At night I used to snuggle in bed with her and wrap my arms around her big belly. She was heavy and moved gently. She was a woman of few words and I think that I mostly communicated with her nonverbally. There was a mutual understanding and bonding between us as if she was reading my thoughts, knowing my soul's desire. I knew that she understood my passion about life and she understood why I had not been able to work at the box factory. When I looked in her eyes and dreamed of being all that I could be, I knew that she saw that part of me, that embryo, that creative drive that longed for fruition. My inner struggle had a nurturing nest in her and I always felt the safety of her arms and her round body.

Grandmother rarely mentioned my mother's name but I knew she loved her with all her heart. I did not sense any anger or resentment toward her daughter, only a deep sadness. She loved her children and she used to ask me about my brothers and sister. She used to ask me about my future plans and I could tell that she admired the spark of independence in me.

"I was born with a dream," I once told her. "Sometimes, I don't know if I have the dream or the dream has me. It lives in me." I was surprised to hear myself saying that. It felt as if the words had their own life. She smiled quietly and stared at me with her eyes lit up.

"What kind of dream do you have, my child?" she asked. She extended her arms toward me and hugged me lovingly. I felt a special warmth of acceptance from her. Before I was able to answer her question, however, she continued. "Let your dream speak. Women can have dreams, too."

To hear this from my grandmother had a special significance considering the fact that she was from the old generation, born in Baghdad. The Jewish community in Baghdad held a very profound place in Jewish history and tradition. It went back to the Babylonian 'Golden Age' when in 605 BC Nebuchadnezzar II, the son of Nabopolassar, became the ruler and reigned for forty-four years. In 587 BC, the Babylonians destroyed Jerusalem and carried the leading citizens of the Kingdom of Judah as prisoners to Babylon. It was believed that my family was among those Jews taken to Babylonia. While in exile, God encouraged the Jewish people through the prophets Ezekiel and Daniel to keep the hope and love for Israel alive. Thus it was that many believed they would be returning one day to the homeland. In 1948, after Israel became an independent state, the entire Jewish community left Baghdad and returned to their homeland leaving everything behind. My grandmother and my entire family were among the immigration to Israel that year. I was five years old.

"Women need dreams, too," my grandmother repeated. "Yet, it was not customary in my day for girls to have lofty aspirations. In Baghdad, the Jewish community raised their daughters to be simple and modest. They were taught to take care of their husbands and children. The highest duty was to continue this tradition and raise good children to continue the next generation. Any attempt to change this would have caused much struggle and shame."

"What kind of ideas and dreams did my mother have?" I inquired softly.

"She wanted to go to school. She wanted to learn to read and write." Grandma paused. "Mind you, I had no problem with that but your grandpa would not hear of it at all. Back there in Baghdad they did not believe that a woman needed reading and writing. She was meant to cook and take care of the household."

"Well, she could read a cookbook," I jokingly added.

My grandmother laughed in agreement. "But now we are in our promised land, a land of freedom and understanding, and so girls go to school and can have 'dreams,'" She paused. "I just don't know how it's all going to work together."

Her words would follow me for many years to come.

One day, as we were visiting my Aunt Doris, there was talk about our family's life in Baghdad. My aunt spoke about her mother with overt pride. "In Baghdad, your grandmother owned many buildings," she said to me with nostalgia. "She was a well-known landlord in the Jewish community. Almost everyone knew her because she was so very good to needy people. She would let them stay in her building for a very small rent, or no rent at all." She smiled and looked at my grandmother.

"How many buildings did she own?" I asked quickly, thirsty to hear more.

"Many." She looked at my grandmother from the corner of her eyes as if she was asking permission to continue. Grandma smiled and nodded her head without a sound.

"How many?" I thrust in again.

"Oh, a whole block. Many apartment buildings," she beamed. "I remember," she continued with renewed energy, "that people used to envy us. Your grandma was a very rich and influential woman in her time."

"Oh Grandma, how did you get to be a landlord?" I breathlessly asked. I could not wait to hear how women in Baghdad became landlords and accumulated wealth. I was fascinated.

"It was not an easy thing, especially not for a woman, my child."

"I know, I know. So how did it all happen?" I looked back and forth between my aunt and my grandmother impatiently waiting for their reply.

"She was a very respected woman," my aunt assured me promptly. She looked at my grandmother fondly.

Finally, my grandmother spoke up. "I was my mother's right hand. She was a very wealthy fabric merchant and a smart businesswoman—way ahead of her time." She continued softly as if she was talking to herself. "My mother loved the art of buying, selling and closing a deal. As for me, I recognized the value of investing in real estate. 'You see,' I told my mother, 'nothing is as solid and sure as a real estate investment. People always need a place to live. Housing will always be desirable and going up in value.' She listened to me because it made sense to her and being the kind of woman she was, she gave me almost a free hand. We first bought one small building close to the bakery in a fairly good neighborhood." My grandmother's voice had become clear and strong. I could tell that she was enjoying reminiscing about her past. She was proud of her achievements.

"Do you miss those days?" I asked.

"Yes, I miss them some, but it was not our country. We were not free people then," she added sadly. "We had to leave everything behind." She wrinkled her forehead and wiped her mouth with her palm.

"But your life back then was so full of activity," I said. "It must have been so exciting for you. What about your father? What did he do for a living?"

She paused. "My father was a good man but not a go-getter. You know my mother was the one to make the deals. But he used to join us wherever we went. It was important to have him with us. He was the man, you know. We knew he had to be with us like a protection. But all that is in the past now," my grandmother concluded. I could tell that she was not so comfortable talking about her father.

"Still I would like to know more," I said. "I'd like to hear more about you and your mother. And your father—did he work with you?"

"Oh yes, he helped. Did he work? Well I am not sure you could say that. You see he was very handsome and charming. He was a good-hearted man and everyone who knew him loved him, but he was not a hard worker. He loved the money my mother made. He was a spender. But, it was really my mother who did the work. It was she who made the money. Yet, he was the boss. He was the man, after all." She whispered the last few sentences to us even though no one else was in the room.

"It is such a wonderful story," I said. "It is so exciting to learn more about the women in my family." Once again, I felt that special link to my grandmother.

"Yes, our family was very wealthy," my aunt said with a dreamy look in her eyes.

"So tell me more please, Grandmother," I whispered and moved closer.

"So I married your grandfather. He had a tobacco shop where I used to help him, and then I would invest the money in real estate, of course." For a moment the passion came back into her voice again but then it slipped away as she stared off across the room. "But it is all gone now. We had to leave everything and run." She was referring to the time when Jews were exiled from Iraq in 1951 after the establishment of the Israeli Jewish state. "Now we are free in the land of Israel. It is a miracle. We have our own land and we are self-governing."

Later, Doris pulled me toward the kitchen and whispered to me, "It is not easy for her. You see that she hardly speaks the Hebrew language and she doesn't have her buildings anymore. She feels strange in Israel even though she knows it is a good thing that we have our own homeland... but she has paid a high price. She has lost her passion."

I wondered then if that was the reason she was so very quiet most of the time. It had to be hard feeling so uprooted from her achievements and her enthusiasm. Maybe that was why she used to watch me silently with such understanding. She recognized that passion in me and remembered it in herself. Once she said to me, "You just keep on doing what you're doing. You just keep on doing the right things!" I smiled back at her feeling good inside. Little did I know what fate had in its plans for me.

CHAPTER 6

My Father

To avoid criticism do nothing, say nothing and be nothing.
—Albert Hubbard

The next time I saw my father was spring of the first year of my teaching. It was during Passover vacation about six years after I had first left our little city of Ramleh. The time felt ripe for a visit to Celina and my father. I took the bus from Kiryat-Gat and got off at the central bus station in Ramleh. Walking through the city, as I made my way to our apartment building, carrying my briefcase close to me knowing it held my teacher's degree. *I might need it to prove to Celina that I was not so stupid*, I thought to myself.

I remembered every nook and cranny. After all, this was where I had grown up. Not too much had changed since I left. I looked toward the sand hill and I could tell it was still there with the white rock still wedged in the same position facing up.

This was such a long awaited day. As I got closer to our neighborhood, my steps became slower and somewhat hesitant. All of a sudden I recognized Simcha. She was pushing a stroller with a baby in it and toddling after her was a child about two years old, pulling on her skirt and whining monotonously, "I want ice cream. I want ice cream... I want ice cream now. Now! Now!" Simcha did not pay attention to her little boy and just kept pushing the pram before her. I paused and looked to make sure I was seeing correctly.

"Simcha. Simcha, do you remember me?" I cried and caught up with her.

She stopped the stroller, sized me up and down, and exclaimed, "Oh my God, Sara, look at you. What a lady. You look so sophisticated."

"Thank you," I said feeling very pleased with myself.

"But what are you doing here? You don't look like you belong here anymore," she observed.

I laughed with satisfaction and bubbled out to her like the young girls we used to be, "Simcha, it is good to see you. Tell me, how are you?" My eyes beamed at her and her children.

"Well, as you see, I did get married," she said and pulling a pacifier from her bag, pushed it into her whining son's mouth to quiet him down.

"Yes. I see. That's what you wanted. How is it?"

"Oh, it's good, very good," she replied and smoothed her son's hair.

"He's cute," I said.

The child looked at me with his big eyes and kept sucking on the pacifier, still holding on to Simcha's skirt. "And you? Are you married?" she asked finally.

"No, I am not married!" I smiled thoughtfully. "I am a teacher. This is my first year teaching."

"A teacher? Wow, really? You're a teacher? I can't believe that. It's incredible... A teacher." She seemed very impressed. She looked at me closely and said, "I remember you wanted to learn... you made me swear not to tell your stepmother. I remember. And I could not understand you. So what are you doing here now?" she inquired.

"I am going to visit my father and Celina," I said.

"She will burst with envy. Maybe you shouldn't go there," she fretted.

"Why not?"

"What for? I mean what good would it bring?"

"I must go," I said. "I promised myself that I would."

"Oh, well, then. Good luck to you," Simcha said smiling. "You're going to need it." She turned to her son and said, "Come on Kobie, let's go."

"Are you going to buy him an ice cream?" I wondered aloud.

"Oh, he's already forgotten about the ice cream," she laughed. But as little Kobie heard the word, "ice cream," he started demanding again, "Ice cream... I want ice cream!"

"I'm so sorry," I cried, rushing in to apologize.

"Oh God, you don't know the trouble I have from this little devil. I wouldn't mind going to school myself instead," she complained shooting an apologetic glance at me. With mixed feelings I watched her make her way down the street tending to her two little charges.

I turned and made my way to my father's home. As I entered the apartment hallway, I noticed it seemed much smaller than I remembered it from my childhood. I looked at the mailboxes and saw that my father's name was a bit faded. I passed my hand over it nostalgically remembering the day we had moved into this apartment, and when my father had pasted the nametags on. It seemed like such a very long time ago. My father had still been with my mother then and things were so different. I walked toward the front door and knocked lightly. "It's open." I heard Celina's voice from behind the closed door.

I entered and said, "Shalom." A heavy silence hung in the room. My father was sitting in his armchair sipping hot tea. Celina made her way quietly from the kitchen. They looked at each other and then their eyes fell on me.

"Shalom," my father ventured at last shooting a hurried glance at Celina. "Sit." My father pointed to a chair nearby.

"Why do you come now? We did not see you all those years. You didn't care about us all those years, why now?" Celina demanded, her voice growing louder.

"I just came to tell you that I am a teacher now. I graduated in June." I looked at my father and pulled the chair closer to him.

"That's good," he said.

"I just want you to believe in me, Dad." He looked away, but I kept speaking to him, ignoring Celina. "It is very important to me, Dad, that you believe in me." I felt myself almost pleading for his love.

"Ah… It is so very important to you," Celina burst out repeating my words slowly. "If he was important to you, you would have done what he wanted you to do six years ago and not left him," she attacked. I saw my father looking at Celina, listening and paying attention to what she had to say, and I suddenly realized the futility of it all. I pulled my chair back and watched them. She kept building up her case and he kept listening and I realized I was outside their little circle. "The last time we heard from you,

you wanted a blanket. What do you really want now?" she demanded.

"Enough of that," he said to Celina. I watched him closely. The rings under his eyes seemed darker than ever before. He bent his shoulders forward, grabbing his tea cup in his hands and took a long sip as if nothing out of the ordinary was going on. I noticed his hands were shaking slightly. His face seemed to have an almost frozen expression.

Celina stopped talking for a moment but she remained in the room. She put her hands on her hips and to the accompanying sound of her golden bracelets she pointed at me and stated abruptly, "I don't want her in my home."

My father remained silent as if she was not speaking to him. In the meantime, I got up from my chair ready to leave. "Sit down, Sara." He took charge, as if he had a change of mind. "Will you have some tea with me?" He looked at me and a small smile curled at his lips.

Tears almost choked me and I slowly lowered myself back onto the chair. I felt a wave of happiness and sorrow.

Happiness for his smile, indicating some acceptance. Sorrow, because I became aware one more time in my life how much I needed his love. How much I had missed him and wanted to be hugged by him. How much I wanted to feel his body's warmth and caring. How much I wanted to be his child, untroubled and protected. After my parents' divorce I had taken over the responsibilities of a mother. I used to say to myself, "I don't need anyone. I can do anything alone."

Suddenly, I realized my denial. I sat in front of my father with the tears falling down my face and my father had to look away. The hurt was too deep and still very fresh. I wondered if he felt my pain.

Celina once more interrupted. "We don't need you here. We've had peace and quiet since you left. You are nothing but a troublemaker. You go to your mother's mother in Tel Aviv and then you come to spy for them. I know everything about you. You don't fool me anymore. Do you meet your mother there? Is her boyfriend still with her? Or does she have a new one?" I could see from the look on her face that she was enjoying mocking me. "Everyone here knows who your mother is. Like mother, like daughter, eh?"

Her words rang in the air for sometime as we sat in silence. Her last statement was a deep belief around here. It was like the mark of Cain. My father and his family feared it, too. I felt like I would never be free from this legacy. Indeed, everyone here knew. Most of Ramleh's population were Iraqi Jews who immigrated to Israel in 1951, a few years after Israel's war of independence. You could not hide here. Certainly everyone knew everything about everybody. Some of the families knew each other from as far back as when they lived in Baghdad together at the Jewish quarter.

Yes, my mother's behavior had been unacceptable and offensive. She had had an affair with a younger man, an acquaintance of my father's. Even I could not defend my mother's behavior. I used to see them kissing and hugging while my father was away. Sometimes they used to bribe me. My mother would hand me a few coins asking me to keep "our secret" to ourselves. "No one should know!" she used to say.

I used to feel bad for my father hoping he would never find out, praying for my mother and her lover to stop, wishing for him to go away and vanish. He used to ride a motorcycle and I could hear him coming from far away. I remember feeling self-conscious seeing the neighbors watching. It was dreadful and very shameful and I knew she was betraying my father and breaking the rules. I was a witness to her infidelity and felt as if I, too, took part in her sin. It was hard for me to feel whole. I was only 11 years old and already I had a burden to carry. A secret to hide!

Often my mother used to talk about how young she was when she gave birth to me. "I was only sixteen when you were born, Sara," she would say with melancholy. "I was too young. All I really wanted was to have fun with my girlfriends. But that was not allowed back in Baghdad. Girls grew up to be somebody's wife and mother. That's all. Well, I wanted more than that. Is that such a crime?" she would ask about her lost youth. "Before I married your father I wished to go to school. But that was out of the question for girls. My father would not hear of it. I used to run after my brother, Abraham, and beg him to teach me the letters. I used to have lots of fun and laugh with his friends who were all from fine families. I could have been somebody and married anyone I wanted. When I was young, I was very desirable—many men wanted me."

She always had the feeling that she could have done better than my father.

And then she met Momo, a handsome, carefree biker. He used to tell us all about his war stories with the Arabs, his heroic acts at the borders, and his involvement with war generals. It was all too fascinating and my mother used to listen to him with a look of rapt admiration on her face. He captured her attention and her heart. He became her "somebody!"

First, he got friendly with my dad. He spoke to him with respect as a young man speaks to an older one. He was very helpful and seemed to know everything. He would speak with confidence and always had an example to back up his knowledge. I used to watch him closely and could tell that he was mostly bragging, trying to impress someone. But, that someone was not my father.

I used to watch him with discomfort. If only someone would ask me. You didn't have to be very smart to see what he was after. His was a strange energy. He was an intruder. But, I was too young to be taken seriously. I remember watching him quietly and hoping I was wrong.

My father liked his help around the house and naively thought he had found a good friend. Working nights as a baker and arriving home early in the morning trying to get some sleep did not help. My mother was taken in by Momo's looks and charm and, of course, she believed the heroic stories he told. I used to wonder why my parents, whom I assumed were intelligent people, could believe the far-fetched stories he would present. I particularly did not trust his story about the night he fought eight Arab terrorists single-handedly and brought them in to the nearest police station.

"I had my gun on my belt but I did not need to use it," he said, making sure that he pulled it out to show it off.

"Wow, you have a gun?" my mom exclaimed aloud.

"Oh, yes," he chuckled and brushed his hair from his forehead with pride.

"Is it legal to have a gun these days?" my father wondered with concern.

"Nope, and I don't care. No one will mess with me. I've had it since I was thirteen," he laughed again. "No one messes with Momo," and he pointed his finger to his chest with smugness.

"How do you think I was able to take on the terrorists? They surrendered to me like lambs." He glanced at my mom who listened with astonishment. She was full of admiration for his courage and strength and went on to ask him with great concern whether he had gotten hurt at all.

"Just a little bit—nothing I couldn't handle," he replied quickly. "In fact," he added, "later on I was rewarded by the government of Israel but it is something that I don't like to advertise or talk about very much because the entire action was considered a military secret."

Once I remember him speaking about his childhood with considerable self-importance. He was the youngest of six brothers and, according to him, he was the most loved and treasured. He grew up without a father and considered his oldest brother to be the authority in the house.

"I always used to speak my mind and even my big brother could not tame me," he said proudly. "I am uncontrollable."

Often, he was invited to our home for the Sabbath dinner on Friday night, as my father did not work on Friday nights. He would stay late eating, talking and drinking wine even after my father would doze off on the sofa. He and my mother would talk about his great tales and possibilities for the future. Momo spoke about the feasibility of starting a business in leather goods because he had connections and he knew he could do anything. He kept on telling my mother about the fortune they both could make.

"Your husband's work is hard and not so profitable," he commented.

"Yes, it is hard work… Look at him," my mom agreed. "He can't even stay up to enjoy an evening with us."

"That can change," he promised.

"He is tired. That's why he sleeps and besides it is late," I volunteered.

"Why don't you go to sleep if it is so late?" Momo asked nicely.

"I am not tired at all," I responded and got up to sit on the couch close to my dad. My brothers and sister had gone to bed hours before but I was afraid to leave my mother alone with Momo.

"The night is still young," he said while opening the second bottle of wine. He then lit a cigarette and handed it to my mom. He was a heavy smoker and sometimes he would light his new cigarette with the end of the old one. He took a deep breath and seemed to enjoy the smoke as it filtered through the silent room.

Glancing at my father, my mom said apologetically, "My husband either works or sleeps. There is not much in-between."

Her comment was said seriously with no humor but they both laughed loudly. It was a clear indication that she was displeased with my father. "He is boring," she confirmed, sipping her wine and shrugging her shoulders.

"You are very beautiful," he murmured quietly and my mother's eyes lit with pleasure.

"What really bothers me most about him," she said to Momo "is that he is not very sharp. Everything is very plain and simple for him." She didn't seem to be concerned that my father might hear any of this. He was sprawled asleep on the sofa across from them.

I moved closer to him and held his hand.

"What are you doing?" my mother asked. "He is asleep." I kept quiet and did not move, just kept my hand on my father's arm, noticing how tranquil and relaxed he looked.

How unaware of what was taking place. How trusting he laid there as he innocently surrendered his fate to the hands of an outsider.

My mom was like a child, restless and full of energy. Her only concern was to have fun and enjoy the moment. She put aside her responsibilities as a mother and a wife. She put aside her reality and fully engaged with the sweet moment of fantasy. I watched her face that was beaming and full of joy. She had the attention of a younger man whom she believed was everything women desire. He had called her beautiful and she felt it.

As I watched her with Momo, it was pretty clear that she was not bored anymore. He made her laugh and promised her a life of fortune and glamour.

I looked around the room at the two men and realized with a sinking feeling that they could not be more different.

Celina's words broke through my reverie as she repeated again, "We don't need you here anymore. You left your father like your mother did and we don't need you."

I watched my little brother, Avi, hiding his tiny body behind my father's chair. Suddenly his face got longer and his eyes opened wide. He looked terrified of what might happen next.

As I was trying to compose myself, the door opened and my ten-year-old brother, Carmel, walked in. He had three heavy soda bottles in his hands and his shoes were worn out at the heel. His trousers revealed a deep cut that had not scarred.

"What is that?" I asked worried.

"It is from the soda bottles," he said and sat on the floor. "I work at the soda bottles factory now," he hurried on to explain, speaking with pride.

"Father, he is only ten years old." I turned my head and looked at my father.

"He wanted to work, to help, but he still goes to school. He works only in the afternoon."

There was a strong urge in me to take charge and fight for my brother's rights but I remained quiet. My face was an open book, however, and revealed me. Celina burst out, "You see, she will spoil everything! Look, you will not run this house. We have had peace for nearly six years. Now you better leave."

But, I did not move. I only called my brother to come sit next to me. Putting my hand on his shoulder, I asked, "How did it happen?" and put my hand gently on his leg.

"One of the soda bottles burst. It made such a big boom and the glass from the bottle got in my leg. I took out the piece of glass and finally the blood stopped." He pointed at the wound and said proudly, "It's okay now; it doesn't hurt anymore."

"You don't have to work, you know," I said to my brother.

"But I want to work. I want to help Daddy. I am not going to leave him like you did!" I was silent for a long moment. I looked around and it became very clear to me. I was not needed here. It was time for me to leave. I said goodbye to my father and stooped down to kiss my ten-year-old brother on his forehead.

What could I say to my brother who wanted to please his father at all cost? How could I disagree with his strong need to be approved and loved by his daddy? He was ready to pay the high price and I admired him for striving to get what was so dear and important to him. After all, isn't that what I had done at his age? I felt a wave of love and admiration toward him.

I turned around and hugged Avi's trembling body close to mine for a long moment, then stood up and turned back to leave.

As I slowly walked through the town, I remembered Simcha's words earlier that day. "You don't look like you belong here anymore."

CHAPTER 7

The Meeting

Nobody objects to a woman being a good writer or sculptor or geneticist if, at the same time, she manages to be a good wife, good mother, good looking, good tempered, well-groomed, and unaggressive.
—Leslie M. McIntyre

I think that inside each of us dwells a divine spark. A part of our Creator resides in our being. It is pure and wholesome. It is loving and compassionate and, above all, it is nonjudgmental. It is the part that puts us in touch with the notion that everything is possible, yet we often hold back because of the concern that others will limit it. I believe in my early childhood the innocent child in me naturally followed and obeyed this powerful sense of unlimited possibilities and I was able to express myself fully in spite of my circumstances. Celina could not stop me.

It was very simple. In my early days there was no one to trust, no one to believe in, and no one to talk to. I had to go within. It was here that I found this only friend and confidant. There was a direct and silent connection between this "presence" and me. There was no conflict, no hesitation, no second-guessing. I spoke and acted through this inner primal strength.

As I look back now, the sand hill was the place I went to for meditation and to strengthen my feelings. There I would sit on the big white rock drawing circles in the sand and planning my next move away from Celina's screaming and demands. In a childlike way, in a mood of utter tranquility, I developed an inner strength that slowly grew within me. There was no doubt in my mind that the sand hill and what it represented was my sanctuary. It was the single most solid and reliable place in my childhood.

When I left it, I left behind not only the solace of my sand hill but also the hope of any kind of a bridge between my father and myself. It was a hard time for me and I felt the loneliness of my life more than ever before.

Returning to Kiryat-Gat, it all felt new and I took my first steps cautiously. My weekend visits to Tel Aviv and my grandmother became more precious than ever before. To me Tel Aviv was the heartbeat of the world. I loved this big city. I would arrive on Friday afternoon from Kiryat-Gat and my first stop was always the central bus station in the heart of the city. Many buses would be lining up, ready to take off to different destinations. People were rushing everywhere. Some were coming in from different parts of the country, ripe for new activity and accomplishment.

I always took the #5 connection bus to the northern section of Tel Aviv where my Grandmother Sophie and her son, my Uncle Abraham, lived. I was grateful and satisfied with my life, looking forward to my future. Above all, I felt free. There was such a tremendous power in feeling liberated as a young woman. The road of life opened up before me. I imagined the feeling of a rose when it first opens its petals and takes its initial breath of fresh air.

One Friday night as I arrived for the weekend, I was told that my second cousin was having a party to celebrate his promotion in the army to a higher position. "There will be many young men at the party, the best in town. They are Gideon's friends so be sure to be there," my Great Aunt Beth, Gideon's mother, told me. She had come especially to visit my grandmother and deliver the news. "Sara, it is time for you to find a nice man. You are not so bad looking, you know," she said as she smoothed her hand over my curly hair sending a quick look at my grandmother. They both smiled and nodded their heads in silent agreement.

From early childhood I had appeared on the surface as a strong and assertive individual. At some level, I guess I believed life demanded that from me. But beneath it all, I embraced and cherished my soft and feminine energy. I was extremely sensitive and had a great yeaning for love and affection. Frequently, however, I was more concerned with how others thought about me than what was going on inside. Many times I hushed my inner voice and existed solely in my head. Sometimes I would realize this and feel the sadness of sacrificing my innocent, beautiful self just for the approval and acceptance of others. This went on with my looks as well as my feelings.

So now as I looked at my grandmother and my aunt, I tried to make sense of their worry. "Beauty is not everything, you know," I finally said to them with some authority and confidence.

"It is if you know men," my aunt laughed. "In fact, that's all they see at first. But you are not so bad. You have a nice body," she said pointing to my breast line and tapping me lightly on my behind.

"My God, you are sizing me up as if I was for sale," I said and moved away.

"In reality, we are for sale," she said, "even though we don't want to believe it. But this is how they will size you up. This is how things are, you know." She paused as if she was thinking over her own life. "Don't ever say I told you this. It is an unspoken truth but I will never say I said it," she concluded.

"Why not?" I inquired.

"What do you mean 'why not?' It's shameful to think that way," she said.

"So why then do you think this way?" I asked.

"Because it's the naked truth. Men give us what we want which is security and we give them what they want which is our body. Call it love if you wish. But that is the trade off. That is the naked truth, my girl." She breathed sharply and let out a deep sigh.

"I don't think so. Love is love. It is not a business. You cannot buy and sell it!" I cried, speaking as an expert.

"You are still so young," my aunt said with a smile.

"Sha. Sha. That's enough for today," my grandmother interjected. She could see that I was struggling to digest what my aunt had said. She could see that it troubled me.

The night of the party I was still deciding what to wear. Most of my clothes were conservative and dull. I looked at my grandmother's wardrobe and pulled out a woolen gray dress. It was oversized but I managed to gather it at the waist with an old-fashioned red belt. I twisted the soft red leather around the gold buckle at the center of the belt and smoothed the skirt down. It looked unique and not too pretentious. I looked at myself and was content. As I glanced at the mirror, I could see my grandmother's pleased expression.

"What do you think?" I asked excitedly twirling around like a little girl. I felt happy and, more importantly, I felt beautiful. I jumped up and hugged my grandmother's big shoulders. "Do you think I look nice?" I insisted, fishing for a compliment although deep inside I did not need her confirmation. I felt beautiful for the first time in my life and that was enough.

"Now don't stay too late. Ladies don't stay until the end of the party," she cautioned. "I spoke with your Aunt Beth and asked her to have Gideon escort you back home no later than eleven o'clock."

"That's okay with me," I said sincerely and started off on my way. I took the bus from my grandmother's home and got off at the fourth stop. As I approached my aunt's house, loud music and bright lights flowed from the windows. For a moment I felt uncomfortable and almost turned to go back. As much as it excited me, I was not used to life in the big city. But I took a deep breath and pulled the big gate open at the entrance to the garden. My aunt greeted me at once with a wide smile and introduced me to a group of girls who all seemed to be talking loudly and laughing. They nodded their heads briefly and resumed their conversation.

I noticed that the girls were meticulously dressed in silk and other soft fabrics. Many of them had low neckline tops. I remembered my aunt's earlier conversation and tried to dismiss it with an inner smile. They were wearing jewelry and their hair was arranged according to the latest fashion. Their faces were made up with rouge and loud colors of lipsticks, something that I had not tried yet.

Suddenly, I felt uncomfortable with my woolen gray dress and hoped they would not notice that it was my grandmother's. I wished not to be seen and I quickly lost the cheery mood I had just had at my grandmother's house. I overheard my aunt saying, "She is my second cousin," and then she threw a few words to me over her shoulder. "Get something to drink and mingle."

I smiled and nodded my head, slowly walking toward an empty chair at the end of the room. I sat down trying to assume an air of confidence, hoping to blend in with the crowd. Looking around the room, I saw that almost all the men were wearing dark suits or sports jackets. A few were in army uniforms. Almost all had a drink in their hands. Some of them were telling jokes and flirting while others were passionately sharing their political opinions. It all was very new to me. This was my first co-ed party and watching the men was fascinating. Most of them stood tall and seemed to be so sure of themselves. To me they looked unreachable, almost immortal, as if they were a species from another galaxy. I giggled to myself as I thought of the way I viewed them.

Scanning the room with my eyes, I eventually honed in on one of the men. He was tall and slim with dark hair, a high forehead and big brown eyes. He was leaning against the wall holding his drink in his hand and staring at me with a slow, easy smile. I lowered my eyes with some embarrassment and felt a blush covering my entire body. I squirmed in my chair anxiously, trying a new position: uncrossing my legs, and then crossing them again in the opposite direction. I pulled my skirt down, raised my head up and dared to look at him again. He was still staring at me. Our eyes met for a short moment and I felt a burning throughout my body. He burst into laughter and moved his body forward away from the wall. His penetrating look left no doubt in my mind that he was going to approach me at some point. Our eyes met again and he started to move from his place walking with assurance toward me. Pulling up a chair, he sat down next to me continuing to hold onto his glass.

"You are very quiet," he said. He, too, was wearing a dark suit, white shirt and a black tie. He smiled and waited for my answer.

"I don't have much to say," I said finally in a whisper, looking up at him and absorbed in the movement of his lips.

"I thought so," he murmured and moved his chair even closer. "I like a quiet girl," he added and took my hand.

I was surprised, not knowing what to say, and I pulled my hand away from his. "Are you drunk?" I asked glancing at his glass.

"No, I don't usually drink," he laughed. "This is milk. I am still a kid at heart." We laughed together and I felt instantly more comfortable. "I am Dan," he added and reached out his hand to shake mine.

"Sara," I smiled noticing his long fingers and skinny hands. I liked the way his hair gently fell on his wide fore-head. He had a pleasant smile and as he grinned his thin mustache spread along his face. He had a smart and distinctive look that was softened by the easy smile that played around his mouth. I don't recall feeling butterflies in my stomach as I used to read in some romantic stories, but I knew I felt wanted and desired which was more than I had ever experienced before.

"Would you care for a drink?" he asked gently while leaning in toward me.

"No thanks. I don't drink," I said.

"I figured you didn't but I'll bet there is still milk in the refrigerator." He glanced at me from the corners of his eyes and I noticed that they crinkled when he smiled. "The next dance will be a slow one. You will dance with me? I don't dance any other dances," he explained quietly and waved his hand toward the man in charge of the music. "Hey, Omer, put on some nice, slow music for me, will you?"

And so we danced. It was my first dance with a man and I felt myself blushing and catching my breath. I was glad it was a slow dance. I put my hand on his shoulder and followed his lead. In the Hasidic boarding school we had never been allowed to spend any time with boys or to look straight into their eyes. I was taught to look down when I spoke to a man. That was one of many modesty rules. We also could not wear short-sleeved tops. The sleeves had to cover our elbows and our skirts had to be long enough to cover the knees. And yet, here I was dancing in the arms of this stranger. The music went on and eventually I could see my aunt trying to catch my eye from the sidelines. She motioned me over excitedly. I mumbled some excuse to Dan and left him by the side of the room.

"Do you know that young man you are dancing with?" She pulled me by the hand and took me to the corner.

"No," I said as I looked at Dan behind her shoulder.

"He is a very well-known journalist, a wonderful young man and a good friend of Gideon's. I myself…" my aunt held her words back as she talked fast and looked at me almost with envy. She leaned closer to me and whispered, "He is a good catch!"

"I just met him," I said, surprised by my aunt's reaction. "He did say though that he likes quiet girls," I added.

"Just don't be a fool. Hold on to him," she muttered pushing me with her elbow. "He is a sophisticated man who has his fingertips on the pulse of the world." She was breathing deeply. "He is someone who could understand you. Imagine that."

That hit home. *Someone who could understand me. Maybe he would understand my ambitions, too. Imagine that!* I smiled to myself and felt a flush of excitement.

Dan stayed with me all that evening. He seemed to take a great interest in me and toward the end of the party he asked my aunt if he could escort me to my grandmother's home.

While we leisurely walked, Dan told me about his work as a journalist and a specialist in Israeli/Arab affairs. "It is very intense and, as long as the Arab countries stay around, I will always have plenty of work," he said smiling. Then he asked about me. "Tell me about yourself," he said.

"My stories aren't interesting like yours. They're not exciting like yours," I said, blushing. Like a hand reaching from the past, I felt less than.

"I want to hear them. I want to know everything about you. Where are you working? What made you decide to go into teaching? Everything…"

I told him about my work, my students and the special education program that we were introducing in the south of Israel. He listened closely and I felt important. For the first time I felt like I had something to contribute, too. Finally, he asked, "How would you like to write an article about the new educational program at your school? I have heard about it recently and I shall see to it that it's published in my paper."

"Me?" I said stunned, and he nodded his head with a smile.

"You can do it," he said patting my shoulder.

I remember feeling an influx of strength and I tried to recapture my old dreams when I used to sit on the sand hill in my village. Then I would imagine creating all kinds of things and reaching out to the world in exciting, courageous ways.

"All right. I'll do it!" I blurted out. "I will write you an article and I'll mail it to you." I felt so full of energy that I skipped and jumped up and down lightly like a child. Life was suddenly happening and I felt a part of it. Dan noted his address on a slip of paper and handed it to me eagerly.

"I will be waiting for your article. Don't forget." By then, we were very close to my grandmother's home. He escorted me to the door, held my hand for a moment and then was gone.

Three weeks later I saw my name printed prominently over my article in the newspaper. That Saturday night I met Dan in Tel Aviv. It was a hot summer night and an easy humid breeze played in the air. We had dinner at a small restaurant by the shore overlooking the Mediterranean Sea. I was wearing a white sleeveless blouse I had purchased that Friday when I arrived in the city. I loved the feel of the silky fabric against my skin and adored the lacy ruffle around the neckline. Purposefully, I pulled the lace over my neck and gathered my hair in a French twist. I enjoyed my feminine energy and could feel the inner glow of confidence exuding from my core. Life was good. I had just published my first article and was escorted by a man who was acknowledged and loved by everyone. I sat across the table and faced Dan with a smile. I noticed the spark in his luminous black eyes. He stretched his long legs from under the table and leaned back.

"You look divine this evening," he murmured.

"Thank you," I smiled quietly and stared at him with gratitude.

"You have the beauty and the talent."

I lowered my head as I felt the warmth of my blush. Beauty? Did he say beauty? It was difficult for me to take in as no one had ever called me beautiful before. I realized he was still talking.

"You've got to write more. You definitely have the talent. I didn't even have to correct much of your article."

"You really think so?" I finally asked.

He nodded his head with a definitive yes. The evening felt magical.

Over dinner, he spoke to me quietly, telling me at length about current events and about an interview he had just had with the chief of staff. He invited me to come to the editorial office to see what made up a newspaper. He was so sweet to me and treated me like such a special person. Toward the end of the evening, he leaned toward me and drew his hand over my bare shoulder. "Your skin is smooth as silk," and I felt a quivering in my stomach. Nerves or desire—I could not tell.

Our meetings became more frequent and I received flowers and gifts every time we met. He used to bring musty white flowers, especially orchids. "Pure white orchids for my pure little girl," he would say and then he would add, "I love you because you are so naïve and simple. I feel I can mold you the way I want. You are like raw material in the hands of an artist. Can I be your artist, your creator?" He did not expect me to answer. And I did not have an answer for him. I smiled and took his remarks as a great compliment.

Dan wanted to be my creator and mold me. What did that mean? All I could focus on in my naiveté was the fact that he was interested in me.

Later, I would remember the feeling of discomfort that was stirring deep in my gut, but at the time all I could think of was that he loved me.

But would he continue on loving me?

CHAPTER 8

Life is Beautiful

If God lived on earth, people would break his windows.
—Jewish proverb

As time went on, I saw that Dan possessed a tremendous yearning for beautiful things in life. He liked to give and to impress. He loved to spend money. He would say that money should be used, not worshiped. For hours, he would stand in front of store windows, window-shopping, unable to remove his gaze from the beautiful objects displayed, particularly gleaming and expensive items. Furs and diamonds. Silk, muslin and jewelry. He was every woman's dream. And he was mine.

At least twice a week I used to come to Tel Aviv modeling my new dresses for him. We were invited to premieres where I would shake hands with actors and artists behind the scenes and receive compliments from well-known people. I began to read the fashion supplements in the paper, and to keep up with the latest styles. Dan's newspaper would arrive every morning and I would underline his name, skim over his article and then move on to the fashion section. I began to visit the best hairdressers and to shop at the most expensive boutiques. All this was under Dan's expert guidance. He seemed to take such pleasure in my blossoming and discovering the woman inside me.

One day, after spending the afternoon shopping for a dress, Dan hailed a taxi and opened the door for me. "I will pick you up tomorrow evening at six p.m.; we are invited to a dinner party," he said while giving directions and pre-paying the driver. I nodded my head in agreement and sat back in the seat with a big smile on my face and holding onto my beautiful new dress. As we drove, I could see the taxi driver glancing at me through the mirror.

"It's a beautiful day out," he ventured.

I agreed silently and smiled. I couldn't wait to get to my destination and share my good fortune with my grandmother. When I left the taxi in front of my grandmother's home, I carried the dress as if it was a trophy and rushed inside to show it off.

"Grandma, look at what Dan has bought me. You wouldn't believe how much he paid for it! Look at this," I exclaimed pulling the dress from the mounds of tissue paper. "It's the latest style."

My grandmother looked at me with a quiet smile, gently touching the fabric and smoothing her palm over the bodice. "Don't forget, little girl, this is only a thing."

"So?" I asked, still feeling drunk with pleasure.

"So, don't lose your head."

"Oh, I won't. I won't," and I tried to slow down knowing she was right. "But, I would like to try it on for you. Please, Grandma?"

Laughing, she nodded her head. I took off my clothes

and gently reached for the new dress. A creamy pink satin cut on the bias hugged my figure and smoothed its way along my body. An extra silky fabric was twisted along the neckline and framed my chest. It was lowcut and I tried without success to cover my cleavage. Pulling my high heels from under the bed, I stepped into them to complete the look. I walked elegantly before my grandmother and waited for her reaction.

She could not help but be amazed and a pleasurable smile played on her face. "It is beautiful. What a transformation."

"You like it?" I exclaimed, hugging myself and twirling around.

"Don't show it to your Uncle Abraham. He wouldn't let you wear it," she said. "I myself don't understand why Dan would buy you such a sexy dress. I don't understand. It is not good for a girl like you to wear such a low cut dress. After all, you are not married to him yet."

"Yes, but it's the fashion today," I replied with excitement trying to justify his purchase.

"Truthfully, I think you should take it back," she added with some hesitation. "It will put ideas in his head. You know you mustn't let him touch you. You have to be a virgin for your wedding."

"Oh, Grandma, Dan is very respectful toward me. You don't have to worry."

"He is a man. Don't forget that," she added.

"How can I forget that," I laughed. "But you don't have to worry. In fact, we have not even had our first kiss yet."

"That's good," she said with some relief and the subject seemed to be closed.

I kept the dress and the next evening Dan picked me

up at 6:00 p.m. sharp. "You look divine," he said extending his hand to me. I floated down the stairs and took his hand in mine.

At this and other parties, things were not rosy all the time, however. In the company of Dan's friends I was mostly silent, sitting close to him, holding his hand like a frightened child, and feeling very self-conscious. I hardly said anything but would listen mesmerized to their discussions admiring the way they all carried themselves. They all seemed to be such achievers and I saw them all as better than me.

"You know, it's hard to imagine Sara standing in front of her class and actually talking," I overheard one of Dan's friends say to him one day. "She is so very quiet."

"I like it that way," Dan responded laughing loudly. Later, however, when they had left, he raised his voice toward me with anger. "It puts me in an embarrassing position. You've got to say something sometimes." It was the first time he had yelled at me and I immediately felt guilty and small. I blushed and promised to try, but inside I felt scared.

Dan was not happy that evening and I did not know what to do to make him feel better. It was natural for me to blame myself for everything. It was such a familiar feeling. "You must talk," he said. "They are not going to eat you alive. What is wrong with you?"

"I don't know them," I said in my defense. Then I swallowed my fear and continued, "I don't really even know you yet."

"Me? I am a colorless journalist! That is all you have to know about me," he exclaimed.

"That is a great achievement, to be a journalist," I retorted.

"An achievement my ass! You must be crazy. I write for newspapers that, in the end, find their way into the toilet. That's where I end up everyday," and he wrinkled his nose with scorn. "Look at me. Do I look like an achievement to you?!"

"Yes," I said quietly, knowing he did not really want my answer. I was puzzled. It seemed so odd to me that Dan would doubt himself like that. It was inconsistent with the image I had of him. Furthermore, I was not ready to take him off the pedestal where I had placed him since the very first night at Gideon's party. Everyone else put him on a pedestal. How was I to think any different? I did not like that Dan would so willingly tear himself down and mar this image I had of him.

As time went on, Dan's usual modulated manner and love and care for me gave me hope. I was able to shift the negative experience from my home with Dad and Celina to a calm loving place with Dan. Gradually, I allowed my heart to open up to him and embrace that early childhood feeling of trust once again. I began to share my thoughts and memories quite often.

Once I told him about the time I had overheard my mother talking with my aunt about the fact that I was so homely, and that she was very concerned that no man would ever desire me. I told him that I remembered promising myself that I would have something more valuable than just outside attraction.

Dan told me that I had all the beauty any man would ever want. He made me feel so special and I would look at him as my protector, the one who'd keep me safe and feeling beautiful forever.

I was totally infatuated with him and taken by the glamorous life he offered me, and the vision of me that he held dear to him. I heard what I wanted to hear and held on to what I wanted to believe.

And so, one afternoon Dan came with me to my childhood village and climbed with me on the sand hill in Ramleh. I felt so free that I skipped all the way to the top of the hill. I showed him the rock I used to sit on as a child and dream my lofty dreams and I shared my "secrets" with him. It was another dream coming true for me—having my man with me on the sand hill and sharing everything with him.

"One day I want to be a well known artist," I told him. "I want to sculpt and paint. I want to express my feelings with these hands. Sometimes, I feel that my hands have a will of their own. They want to create, to express themselves." I extended my hands and looked at them laughing at myself with joy.

"Someday, I would like people, all kinds of people, to be able to touch and feel and see my thoughts." I stood up and continued to speak in a dreamy voice. "I would like to write, too, but sometimes I think words put some kind of limitation on my emotions."

Opening my arms wide, I stretched as tall as I could. "I believe I can communicate with the world. I want to say to everyone that life is beautiful. Even though I did not have it easy as a kid, in spite of it all, I can still show that life is beautiful. Do you know why?"

Not waiting for an answer, I got closer to him, bent lightly and kissed him on his check. Although I had never been drunk before, I felt like I was drunk then with joy… I had the stage and my man was right there listening to me. For the first time there was another person with me on my sand hill and I was sharing my dreams.

"So, do you know why I think life is beautiful? Because there is always tomorrow to make up for today or for yesterday… No one can take away from me that feeling of hope, that belief in myself." Pausing, I looked at him and drew a breath for courage. "I also believe that I am as good and as capable as anyone else." I paused and looking at him expectantly, added, "I am also not less of a human being just because I am a woman." I stopped short and there was deep silence for a while.

When I looked over at Dan, I could not tell his reaction to my words. I walked over next to him and sat down, touching his face lightly with my hands. Nervously, I continued, "Sometimes, I think that GOD must be a woman, like a big loving mother, a mother that gives birth to us all." I looked at Dan and suddenly knew that I had crossed his boundaries. It had taken all of my courage and trust to tell him my secret thoughts, but as I watched him and saw the puzzled expression on his face, I knew I had gone too far. For some reason though, I kept on speaking. To this day I don't know where I found the chutzpah but somehow I continued. After all, I was on my sand hill. Most probably my goddess was with me and these words just flowed out of my mouth. "Sometimes I feel very close to God and it feels as if God is sitting right here inside me." I touched my stomach, and despite Dan's warning look, I was glowing with excitement.

Dan got up and slowly started walking down the hill. I followed him quietly wondering at his reaction. "There is no such thing as God!" he finally said. He stopped walking and faced me. "It is very stupid to think that there is a God. It is a very primitive idea and above that, to think that if there was a God, it would be a woman! What an insult!

What kind of a woman—like your mother or mine?" He took a deep breath and continued with renewed energy. "Women have a long way to go to be a God of any sort. Women have to clean themselves up. They are no GODS. Believe me I know what I am saying. Women are not gods. Not even close," he spit out. He glanced around to see if anyone was listening to what he was saying. Then he composed himself and looked at me quietly. He relaxed, took a deep breath and said softly with his characteristic smile, "On the other hand, you are my dear good girl. You are my woman and I love you. You are not like these other women."

Inside, I felt frozen. I could not feel love at that moment, at least not his love. I moved slowly away from him and shrugged my shoulders. Trying to shake off the uncomfortable feeling, I looked for a way to make it okay. I so desperately wanted this man to be a part of my life that I was willing to ignore the signals going off in my stomach. "You disagree with me that's all," I said trying to push the fear away.

"Yes, that's all. I just disagree with you," he said and put his arms around me. Trying to smooth out what had just happened, I remained quiet and thoughtful. His arms started to feel heavy and I slowly disengaged myself from his hug.

"What are you thinking about?" he asked.

"God," I said hesitantly.

"Will you stop that nonsense," he demanded.

"Why?"

"Because I said so. No woman is God, not even my mother and she is dead!" He became annoyed again.

"Your mother is dead. I am sorry. How did she die?" I asked hoping to smooth out his anger.

"She just died. And that makes me an orphan and that's the end of my story. No dreams, no hopes. She is dead. I thought I told you already that she is dead," he said quietly as if he was speaking to himself. Suddenly, his voice changed and he became childlike.

"I am sorry," I said. "I truly am."

"Sorry? For what? You do not understand. Let's just change the subject."

And we did. And I dismissed my feelings. I felt hurt and confused but eventually I became accustomed to it. After all, I came from a culture that had rules and regulations and women were not considered totally equal partners with men. In my heart I deeply disagreed but I felt I could not change the attitude and the beliefs of all. I slowly began to accept Dan's attitude as part of our relationship. I believed it was something I could live with. After all, Dan was an intellectual and a man of the world. Sooner or later he would come to open up to me as an equal. He could be changed with love and time.

Was I in my right mind to think that I possessed the power to change him? Was I secretly trying to mold and shape Dan as well?

CHAPTER 9

Love in Crisis

If your compassion does not include yourself, it is incomplete!
—Buddha

In the days that followed it was very clear that the next step in my relationship with Dan would be our engagement. We had been dating for over a year now and everything seemed to be heading in that direction. And yet, there was still a gnawing that I felt deep in my stomach that now and then would plague me—I could not say that I was in love with Dan. All I knew about love and sensuality was what I had seen in the movies where lovers would passionately hold each other and stretch across a bed framed in pillows. I didn't have that kind of desire for Dan and we did not embrace ourselves with passion at all. Most of our interaction was considered appropriate and suitable to our traditional dating. Sometimes, I hoped that we would have that kind of passion after our wedding, but for now our encounters lacked the spontaneity and joy of our bodies coming together. Interestingly enough, it was fine with me. I could wait.

In the meantime, Dan took care of me in other ways. He bought me things, many things, that no one in the family ever had before: a fur coat, a gold designer watch, a sparkling evening dress, and tickets to the most desirable events in Tel Aviv. Life felt as though it was too beautiful and exciting to be concerned about "being in love." In any case, love had always been very vague and formless for me. How could I recognize love when it had always been absent?

One afternoon Dan took me to the best dressmaker in town to fit me for an evening gown for a party at the Hilton Hotel. Alfred Hitchcock was visiting in Israel to promote one of his movies and we were among the few to join him after the premier for drinks.

When Dan came to my grandmother's house to pick me up, I was all dressed and ready to go. "You look absolutely beautiful," he said and smoothed his hand over my black silk dress. I loved the compliment even though deep inside I had trouble accepting it.

That night I had my first champagne and Dan took me by the hand to say hello to the famous director. I was thrilled and felt as if the miracles of life were touching me. Later on, when we left the party, Dan whispered in my ear, "I noticed Mr. Hitchcock staring at your cleavage. This is a good dress. It can open all kinds of doors for you." He ran his fingers lightly over the bare part of my breast and concluded, "If I was a woman, I probably would become a whore." He spoke with ease as if he was talking to himself.

I did not understand his remark nor did I care at that moment. I felt the sensation of his touch ripple through my body and wished for him to continue but I did not dare ask for it, nor did Dan seem to want it. I was amazed by the demand of my body.

Usually, Dan was very hesitant when he touched me. He appeared fearful of rejection, which seemed so odd to me since he was so confident in other areas. He would stroke me slowly as if he was troubled and I used to remain frozen in my seat careful not to make a wrong move. Inside, I felt like he was waiting for some kind of signal from me but I was not sure what to do. I felt very inexperienced in these matters and I used to wish for him to take charge and hold me tight. It would have felt so wonderful if he had hugged me close to him and I could feel the warmth of his body next to mine. Instead, neither of us moved, and after a while, I would gently shift my body and remove his hand.

One day, when he leaned over and surprised me with a kiss, I noticed his lips were dry and shaky. I could taste the bitter saliva and smell the odor of a hungry stomach. I kissed him back closing my eyes tight and waited for him to stop. It was not what I had expected an adoring kiss to be but I did not let myself be too concerned. I believed it would change with time when he felt more comfortable with me in that area. *With love and understanding all was possible*—or, so I thought.

My young spirit was too busy thinking about his position in society and the bright lights of the city. Every time I read his name over a news item in the paper, I was overwhelmed with pride and a rush of excitement. It was a heady feeling and one that I savored. *I can tailor myself to whatever it is that I need to be or do as a wife. I can make it work, I concluded.*

I knew that he loved me and that was a very significant fact for me. "He will never leave me," I thought. "I will never be abandoned again." For the first time in my life I mattered to someone. That was more important to me than anything, perhaps it was more valuable than love itself. After all, love was so elusive. The gifts and compliments and the actual presence of Dan in my life were much more concrete.

And so, Dan proposed and I felt honored. There was no question about it, only a notification. "I want you to be my wife," he said.

It was a Saturday night while we were having dinner in a small restaurant by the sea. I saw him looking at me seriously while his feet were nervously moving back and forth. Finally, he said, "Perhaps I should ask for your hand from your Uncle Abraham. After all, you are not living with your mother or father... what a pity for you." He shook his head and laughed nervously.

"My hand?" I whispered brushing off his last remark yet knowing what he meant. I could tell he was uncomfortable and wished to get the formalities over with.

"Yes, your hand. Give me your hand," and he reached for my hand and kissed it lightly. "I will get you the best ring and you will put it on this finger," and he pointed to my ring finger. "But... I have one concern," he stammered. I could see that he felt awkward and it was difficult to sit across from him and watch the discomfort on his face, this man who always appeared so confident and in charge. "I have one concern... You see... I mean, you know... You know what everyone says about your mother... I have a concern that it could happen to us." He waited for my reaction.

I took a deep breath and immediately began to defend myself. Somehow, I had known this would eventually come up. "Oh, you don't need to worry," I responded. "I had such a hard life because of my parents' divorce that I know I would never let it happen to me."

He accepted my explanation with a look of relief. "I'm glad to hear that from you. I know you won't disappoint me." He squeezed my hand and continued. "So, my ring will make you my fiancé, and then we will get married. That will finally make you mine. Legally mine." A wide grin played on his face, while I could not help recall Aunt Beth's view of love.

For me, there was no jumping up and down; there was no excited anticipation. Nevertheless, I was happy that someone wanted me, someone who was respected by all, talented and intelligent. He loved me and wished to make me his wife. He would take care of me and, above all, he would give me a legitimacy that my family never thought I would achieve.

Dan left a large bill on the table and pulled me outside behind him. When we reached the side of the building, he pressed me against the wall, pulled my blouse down and quickly scooped my breast in his hand. I could feel his erection through his clothes and I shivered involuntarily. His lips sucked on my nipple as if he were sealing an agreement. It felt as if all was officially permitted now. This was the first time he had allowed himself to be so intimate with me. Strangely enough, I did not have the same rush of emotion my body had craved in the past. Instead, all I could think about was Dan's shame for me when he had told me about his concern.

The next morning, Uncle Abraham informed me that Dan had called. "Dan asked to meet with me. I think he is *willing* to marry you, you lucky girl." He paused. "It is good for the entire family to have him as a member." He patted me on my shoulder. I felt happy for my uncle but inside it felt as if something was missing.

The preparation for my wedding was very simple. Dan took care of all the expenses and made all the decisions. My family was thrilled. They were not even asked to put up a dowry.

As for myself, I purchased my own wedding dress at an elegant shop on the corner of Alambi and Rinyce Streets in Tel Aviv. There was a bus stop in front of its window and when I used to take bus #5 from the central bus station to my grandmother's home, I always sat by the window. As we stopped by the shop to pick up more passengers, I could not help but look at the beautiful dresses. Each one was unique. When Dan had proposed to me, I knew right away where I wanted to find my dress.

As I entered the boutique, two young girls approached me. "Are you getting married?" one of them asked with a big grin.

"Yes," I responded bashfully.

"Would you like me to show you around or are you waiting for someone?"

"Oh, no, I'm not waiting for anyone. I'm by myself," I replied feeling very independent.

As I remember, I approached the whole procedure of buying a wedding dress as just something I needed to do. I did not feel a sense of anticipation or special excitement. Every bride needs a dress and so, here I was.

"My name is Ruth and I'll be happy to help you. Do you want to rent or buy?" she had asked.

"Rent."

She nodded her head and turned toward the wardrobe behind us pulling a dress out as she turned back. "I think this one will be very suitable for you. Why don't you try it on?"

It was a long white satin dress with straight lines and a layer of heavy lace longer in the back. Small pearls were sewn between the layers of lace and framed the square neckline. It seemed very romantic to me and, when I slipped it on, my mind was made up. "It fits you like a glove," Ruth said. "It looks like it was made for you."

"Yes, it does look good, doesn't it," I murmured.

She brought in a matching veil and I asked her to wrap it up. This was the dress I would be married in. It was as simple as that. It probably was the fastest sale she had ever made.

The evening of the wedding was a clear, cool spring night. My aunts wore new dresses and they looked at me with approving eyes as I stood next to Dan glowing as all new brides glow. Grandmother Sophie had arrived in her special blue velvet dress set off with her diamond pin. My Great Aunt Beth, Gideon's mother, was especially pleased. She came over to me and whispered, "I told you he was a good catch." She glanced at my grandmother meaningfully. Even my mother was there with her husband, Momo, holding his hand tightly as if she was afraid to lose him in the crowd. My sister was sipping on her first champagne. My younger brother, Avi, who was only nine years old, was running around playing with his young friends and now and then I could hear their shrill laughter. Carmel, my older brother arrived late; true to form, he could not find the wedding hall in Tel Aviv.

Sadly, of course, my father did not show up at all. Celina did not allow him to attend. Initially, I felt a pang of disappointment but it did not last long.

Dan's family was represented by only a handful of people. His father stood tall and erect next to Dan and carefully examined the guests as they entered the hall. His

Grandmother Naomi watched Dan with pride and a pleasant smile played on her soft face. While occasionally adjusting her new velvet shawl, she would touch Dan's shoulder with obvious affection. Gadi, the younger brother in his new dark suit, stayed close to his sister and anxiously waited for their aunt to arrive from Jerusalem. They all seemed to behave appropriately and socially correct.

The most successful publishers, newsmen, artists and political leaders were there and they soon occupied my attention. It was a most impressive event and I felt very grateful that Dan had offered to pick up the tab. My family could never have afforded it. They all tried to be on their best behavior as they looked over at me proudly.

A few photographers moved around the hall flashing their cameras and highlighting the more important guests. The music was soft and elegant as dinner was served and a spirit of joy and warmth spread throughout the room. Tables were elegantly set with bowls of flowers and continental cuisine. The smells and the sounds were intoxicating and I floated through the evening like in a fairy tale. Shortly after dinner, people started leaving the hall. The light eventually became subdued and I knew the evening was approaching its end. Finally, the long stemmed roses were removed from the tables and Dan and I took our leave from the remaining guests and family.

An hour later we were on an airplane heading toward Eilat. Dan had made a reservation at a new hotel overlooking the Red Sea. It was a beautiful spring night and a warm desert breeze caressed our faces as we stepped off the plane.

We arrived at the hotel at 2:00 a.m. and, as we checked in, I felt very special and grown up. Finally, I owned my life and myself. I was a married woman and I had a husband who loved me. I had left behind my father's anger and the routine of the boarding school. I smiled to myself when I thought of my family's fear that I might lose my virginity before my wedding and go astray.

In my culture, submission was a necessary thing for women in order to keep everyone happy. But deep inside my soul, I knew differently, and in my naivety I believed I could break the old indoctrination. *Dan is a well-educated man,* I thought. *He is not your average, old-fashioned macho man. He is a college graduate, a journalist, a worldly man.* I kept this thought alive in my heart. My only failure was to understand that a belief has nothing to do with a college degree. I longed for him to see me as an equal partner as I knew I could not ever give up my drive to be all that I could be. I was born with it. There was no doubt in my mind that I had something to contribute to humanity. I was willing to submit to my man but not at the price of denying who I was. I believed that it was possible for the two to go hand in hand. On this night, however, all of these thoughts were in the back of my mind. This night was my wedding night and other thoughts and feelings were in the forefront.

In the hotel suite, Dan walked toward the bedroom, smiling at me while examining the wide bed. He nodded his head and quietly said, "It will do."

I did not know what to expect on our honeymoon. My girlfriend, Shoshana, had just gotten married a few months earlier and she had told me about her first experience with her husband. "It's no big deal," she had said. "It only takes a few minutes for it all to be over." She shrugged her shoulders with some disappointment and added, "I don't know why everyone makes such a big deal about sex."

I thought of her now as I felt the contours of my body under my new lacy nightgown. Inside I felt nervous, yet excited. Caressed by the satin sheets, I laid on the soft wide bed. I was drowsy while at the same time awake with happiness and anticipation. The sensations were all so new: this world full of sweet dreams and wonderful plans for the future. It felt so magnificent. I watched Dan moving across the room, taking off his jacket and then his shirt, glancing at me with his easy smile. He slowly approached me and lowered his sinewy body next to mine. I felt soft, secure, and free. Maybe this was what they called love! My mind and body felt so ready for this first experience as a woman. Turning toward Dan, I caressed his thick hair and pulled him gently toward me. He kissed my cheek lightly and whispered, "You are so beautiful, and you are mine." Stretching, he closed his eyes and told me that we should get some sleep. Leaving his underwear on, he pulled the covers all the way over his shoulders and fell asleep.

I, on the other hand, remained wide-awake. I was so ready to give Dan the freedom of loving me exclusively for the first time, to let him feel the sweet desire of my love. I wanted to stroke his body gently with my hands and surrender myself to him. Turning my head I looked over at his sleeping silhouette on the pillow. He looked so innocent and harmless. How could he be wrong? It must be me who was the impatient one.

I rolled my body away from Dan and gently slipped out of bed. Walking on my toes quietly, I crossed the room and dropped into the armchair by the window. Inside, I was flooded with so many different feelings. There was a part of me that felt hurt and disappointed. I looked down at my nightgown and smoothed my fingers along its silky fabric.

It was a beautiful soft pink with creamy lace on its edges. I had bought it just a few days ago especially for this special night. I looked out the window at the sky above and wondered about this thing called love. Finally, I gave into the exhaustion of the day and returned to bed next to my husband.

In the morning Dan was restless. Moving in bed and trying to find a comfortable position, he raised his body above me leaning on his elbow. He looked at me and then pulled away slightly. "I can't do it. I don't know why. I just can't do it! And you aren't helping me." Pulling the cover up and fixing his pillow, Dan lay on his back and stared up at the ceiling silently for a long time. He appeared nervous shifting his right foot back and forth under the blanket. Finally, he turned his face away from me and softly said, almost as if he was speaking to himself, "I've never done it before." There was a long silence as I wondered how to respond.

"I don't want to talk about it!" he murmured and then started apologizing, saying something about his strength and power. He waved his hand in front of his face and then took my hand and pulled me closer. He was looking at me now like a little kid, feeling sorry for not living up to my expectations. He told me how beautiful I was in my lacy nightgown and then he smoothed his hand over my legs gently. He held my hand and told me how much he loved me and how much he wanted me to believe in him, to be proud of him. He told me how much he had been waiting for the night before, and how he felt like his world was falling apart in the blink of an eye. I kept on reassuring him that it was okay with me and that he should not feel bad.

In fact, at that moment, it felt absolutely fine with me

not to be bothered by sex and not to have to fulfill men's needs. I remembered very clearly the uncomfortable feeling I had had around my grandfather when I was a child. He used to like to touch and fondle me when we were alone. I was around six or seven years of age and I remember feeling torn between the need to please my grandfather and my longing to feel safe. I loved my grandfather. In fact, everyone loved him. He used to tell us fun stories, especially in the winter on cold nights. My brothers and I would get under the covers and he would ramble on and on telling us one story after another. But, I did not like to be alone with him and whenever I was, I would try to escape. It stirred up emotions of being held like a hostage and I ended up with a dirty, uneasy feeling in my body. I didn't understand it and it made my life confusing and frightening.

There were times I hated my mom for letting him baby-sit me. I knew the way he made me feel had to be kept a secret even though I don't remember my grandfather ever forbidding me to talk about it. Later on in life, I always felt that men wanted something from me and that I had to give it in order to be loved and accepted. I always felt torn between those two needs: on the one hand the need to take care of myself and on the other hand the need to please others. For the most part I put the other before me. That was how I survived.

And now, here I was with Dan on our honeymoon. I looked at him asking for my understanding when, in fact, I was relieved. How could I possibly explain to him what was going on inside of me. I looked at Dan's serious face and smiled hoping he would return my smile. But instead, I heard him saying, "You see now how little I am? I am not your knight in shining armor now." He raised himself up and leaned on his elbow. I put my hand on his lips, trying to stop him from belittling himself. He held my palm and kissed it but I could see he was having difficulty keeping his mouth firm, and his eyes began to fill with tears. He hooked his fingers into my hair. "Tell me something good, anything, even if you have to lie to me. Just say something." He was almost begging me.

"I love you, Dan. It's going to be okay. I just know it. In fact, I don't care if we ever have sex." I tried to smile and make light of the situation even as I felt the inadequacy of my young age. Snuggling closer to his body, I pulled the covers around us and prayed that what I had just said was enough.

"You don't know what you're talking about." His voice sounded cold and he drew himself away from me again staring at the ceiling. His feet under the covers were shaking faster than ever and I turned on my stomach hugging my pillow in both arms. I could not see what the huge problem was. I could not see the tragedy and great failure through his eyes. It was only a temporary setback.

But he knew better. All I wanted to do was help but all I knew about lovemaking was what I had learned from some romance stories I had read in books.

As I lay in bed next to Dan, I tried to straighten it out in my mind. The description of sex as a sensational feeling must be exaggerated and overdone. I had read about a climax but never understood the feeling. It was all a mystery to me and I wasn't even sure I was eager to discover it. I was happy with the love letters I had received from Dan, the telephone calls, hugs, kisses, smiles and flowers. As for the rest of it, all I knew was whispering and giggles from my friends. It was something you did when you got married, when you wanted a child, something that bound two people together.

I told Dan that there would be other nights in our life and that I wanted those nights to be beautiful and loving. Inside, I was scared but on the outside I was trying to sound confident and supportive. He listened to me silently, reluctantly nodding his head in agreement. Slowly, he got up from the bed and drew the curtains wide open. The Red Sea lay below reflecting the sun's rays on his face. He stood silhouetted against the window, all six foot, one inch of him and I felt tenderness toward him I had never experienced before. He glanced at the clock and then turned to me and said, "I promise you we will come back here for a second honeymoon."

He touched his forehead lightly. "Right now, I think I have a temperature. I feel like shit. Maybe I'll take a pill." He stretched his body as if he was trying to get out of himself. "I'm tired, sick, or… something. And now I think that you are feeling pity for me. Are you pitying me?" His question hit me strongly and I felt the tenderness fade away. I tried to find the answer for the impossible position he was putting me in. I shook my head no, but as I met his eyes, something deep inside of them was fading. I knew I had to answer quickly before it was too late. I found I could answer him strongly. No, I did not pity him; rather his self-doubt angered me. I resented this game. I shook my head no in response to his question but I held my anger to myself.

Later that afternoon, we walked on the beach trying to put the morning's experience behind us. At first, it seemed odd that Dan didn't mention a thing. When I asked him how he felt, he smiled lightly as if he didn't know what I was talking about. "What do you mean? I feel great," he exclaimed. We laughed and ran in the sand and later showered as we prepared for dinner in the hotel's restaurant. That evening I had my first glass of wine. Lounging by the Red Sea, feeling the desert breeze, Dan asked me lovingly, "Will you try wine for me?"

"I've never had it before," I said shyly, placing my hands on my heart and smiling at the waiter's expression.

"But for me..." Dan said and kissed my hand. He ordered the wine.

I did not like the taste but I enjoyed the effect. As it slowly started to creep through my body, I became aware of feeling more and more relaxed. I began to swirl the translucent liquid in the tall crystal glass while holding it in my hand elegantly. I recalled once watching a movie star do the same thing. Dan was studying me. Something inside of him seemed to light up. He leaned over our little table, took a deep breath and lit a cigarette. Raising his hand, he motioned to the waiter for another drink. Then he offered me his cigarette. I moved away chasing the smoke away from my face. He smiled and said again, "For me..." as if his words were a magic wand. Reluctantly, I took my first puff, coughed a bit and handed it back to him.

I was surprised that Dan was encouraging me to smoke and drink wine. Part of me kind of liked it. After all, it was a sign of freedom, and he was opening new and forbidden doors for me. Nevertheless, it felt strange that he did this. I felt unprotected by him as if he was pushing me to do what I knew very well he did not respect. Perhaps he was testing me, or maybe he was amused by his power over me. Was this what he meant by "shaping and molding me?"

Dan held his glass with both hands, leaning back in his

chair, and studying me. Something deep inside his eyes lit up. "Look at all those people," he said pointing at the dance floor with his glass, "dancing inside that small red lantern like a flock. Let's be one of them." He held my hand and walked me to the dance floor. We moved very slowly almost as if we were standing still. I leaned my head on his shoulder and stared out the big glass window that framed the mountain's jagged red rocks. There were only a few trees visible in the lantern's light but I knew they stretched for miles in the darkness. I felt captured by the magic and beauty of nature. All around us was a world I wanted to be a part of, a world I wanted to sink myself into and reflect back in some creative, imaginative way. I sighed deeply and felt adored by him.

"Are you still here?" Dan asked and drew me closer to his chest.

"All the time," I whispered. There were moments when I felt so close to him.

Eilat was an inviting little city, deserted on three sides with the Red Sea on the fourth. At night you could clearly see the light of Akaba, a Jordanian port city. Across the sea, two cities, two different life styles, two different dreams.

"Do you see the light over there?" he asked pointing his hand toward Akaba while walking back to our table. "I wish we could go over there and share life with our neighbors. One day maybe that will be possible... There is so much to gain with peace and so much to lose in war." He pulled out my chair for me and whispered in my ear, "How about peace between us, my little girl?" He kissed me on my cheek and I touched his face. It was warm and I could feel his tenderness. I kissed him back and traced his smile gently with my finger.

"I did not think we were at war," I said solemnly.

"You smart and powerful girl…" He laughed, happily sitting back in his chair.

A waitress approached, touched his shoulder lightly and whispered, "Mr. Tavor, a call from Tel Aviv," pointing to the small desk in the hallway. Dan pulled his eyes away from mine reluctantly and sauntered out to the phone. I watched him from the opposite side of the room as he put his hand over his right ear trying to escape the noise from the adjacent cocktail lounge. Mostly he was listening. Finally, he spoke a few words and shook his head. I saw him slam the receiver down with a gloomy intensity. He walked back toward our table with hesitant steps. I knew this had not been a business call. His face looked like a storm cloud.

"What is it?" I asked.

"My father." He grabbed his glass and swallowed the rest of his drink in one gulp. "One thing I have learned," he muttered as he got up ready to leave. I followed his steps closely as he continued, "Not all God's creatures are sweet little darlings. Not everyone wants peace."

"What's wrong," I asked again taking his hand in mine. He was sweating.

"Sick!" He raised his voice as we started down the hallway. "The old man is sick."

"We should head back," I said concerned.

"My sister thinks he is just pretending… But, anyway, what does it matter? He needs me." Dan kept my hand in his palm holding me tightly. "I'm sorry, but we have to leave tonight," he said. We took the elevator and walked down the hall to our room. He paused in front of the door, put his hand on the metal numbers and looked at me. "I will always remember this number… 722. He smoothed the number with his fingers. We will be back. I promise… we will be back for our second honeymoon." He put the key in the door and pushed it open with his foot.

Silently, we packed and left for Tel Aviv.

CHAPTER 10

The Other Woman

By all means marry. If you get a good wife, you will be happy.
If you get a bad one, you will become a philosopher.
—Socrates

Dan and I took the midnight flight to Tel Aviv. It was an exquisitely clear night with the dazzling bright moon above us hanging full and serene. Dan had withdrawn into himself and sat pensively. Early the next morning, he had his coffee on the porch at our apartment in Tel Aviv. He was restless and kept getting up to pace back and forth. Finally, he came back into the apartment, stopped by his desk and picked up the newspaper trying to read, but soon threw it back on the coffee table. He could not concentrate.

"I've got to go now," he finally said. "I have to see what's wrong with my father." He approached me to kiss me good-bye.

"Do you want me to come with you?" I asked quietly.

"No. You'd better stay here. I know my father." Dan put his arm around my shoulders as I walked him to the door.

"What does the doctor think is wrong?" I asked him.

"The flu," Dan replied. "A very special flu. It's called the 'my-son-got-married' flu. You'll see," Dan said sarcastically. He looked at his watch and saw that it was almost eight o'clock. "I'll see you later." His eyes darted rapidly to the door. Then he dashed through it and ran down the stairs into the street.

It was a warm spring day and I watched him from the window as he hurried down the street and hailed a taxi. Climbing into the back seat, he lit a cigarette. He was definitely worried and nervous.

I had gotten used to this though. Dan had all kinds of private feelings and thoughts that he never spoke about. I had learned to give him his space but I was always concerned whether he would come out of them well. His gloomy expressions and heavy feelings of despair were very unusual to me, yet this was not the first time that I had witnessed him going into this place. It was not the first time that he had pushed me away emotionally. I had learned my boundaries pretty fast though. There was almost no need anymore to speak about them. I just knew he wanted me to stay away. Whatever the feelings were, he kept them locked inside.

I could see Dan in my mind's eye entering his father's home as if entering a different atmosphere, a space I did not know about until much later. Dan was a changed man in front of his father. "The old man" as Dan liked to call him was a man in his early sixties, tall with broad shoulders. His face was long and always serious. His thin lips were almost always locked together and pulled inward. His cheeks drooped down and his blue eyes were frequently half closed.

It felt to me that he wrapped himself in a heavy energy and pushed life away from him. I remember being very quiet and careful of my movements around him.

At his father's home, Dan was welcomed by his sister and younger brother, Gadi. They both were very happy to see him. The old man was sitting in his armchair with his head down clutching a paper in his locked hands. As Dan entered the room, his father raised his head slowly, looking at Dan with despondency. "It is your mother again. The bitch will never stop coming back and ruining my life." His voice was choked and he begged Dan to come and sit beside him.

His father's anger and helplessness slashed at Dan like the crack of a whip echoing from his childhood. He approached his father slowly, his heart heavy and desperately weary. The honor of his family, the honor of his father... this was the dark, insidious secret that Dan had had to deal with all of his life.

Dan's parents had gotten married in the mid-thirties in Baghdad. It was an arranged marriage. Dan's mother, a beautiful fifteen-year-old girl, came into union with Dan's father, a well-to-do man in his early thirties. He was the owner of a small candy shop in the Jewish quarter in Baghdad and desperately in need of love and affection.

The families made a simple agreement. Dan's father would provide and care for this young girl and her mother as long as they lived. Dan's father gazed into the eyes of this beautiful virgin girl and could not refuse the deal. So Grandma Naomi moved in with her daughter and her new husband immediately after the wedding night. Nine months later, Dan was born.

Life was not smooth and simple, however. It was hard

to control and buy the love and affection of Dan's mother. Eventually, his father's bitterness and control drove her into the arms of a young, successful physician in the big city of Baghdad. Mother and daughter tried to keep the secret as long as possible, but Dan's father knew all along that his young, attractive wife was unhappy with him, and that there was another man in her life. It was almost too dreadful to accept and he bitterly held it against his wife's mother, blaming her for the kind of daughter she had raised. Dan grew up seeing his father's shame and pain and struggled quietly with his own love-hate feelings toward his mother.

In 1951 when the Jewish community migrated to Israel after their declaration of independence, Dan's family was one of thousands on their way to the free land. There was a great hope and relief that now there would be a natural separation between the young wife and her lover. Two weeks after Dan's family arrived in Israel they were assigned to live in Jerusalem, but his mother already had a clear plan of her own to go back to her lover in Baghdad. She was helped across the Jordanian border to meet him there and to start a new life.

Dan's father and the rest of the family secretly declared her dead and moved from Jerusalem to Tel Aviv in late 1951. From then on it was forbidden to mention her name in public or even among members of the family. The matter was closed. There was no discussion. But the wounds were wide open for years to come. There was an unmistakable resentment and anger from Dan's father all of the time, and an open hostility and verbal abuse toward Naomi, Dan's grandmother, who stayed with the family to take care of the children. Although they all tried to make life easier for Dan's father, he used his misfortune to control everyone.

He grew old reminiscing about the good years he had spent with his wife. It was now a measuring stick for his last remaining years. She was living happily with another man while she had left him only with his feelings of insecurity and bitterness. Gradually, over the years, he seemed to have adjusted to it but the bitterness never really left him. It was like a rocking chair cradling his spirit, day in and day out, and there was no one in the family who was not affected by it.

Almost thirteen years had passed since the day she had left. Thirteen years since the old man had shouted on the hills of Jerusalem declaring her dead. But the tension and the feelings of uncertainty kept spiking like lightning through the atmosphere of Dan's world. Even now, when Dan had grown into manhood and was a noted writer, he still was not the master of his own self. He still kept feeling himself pulled back to the shaky kingdom of his childhood.

Now, Dan sat on the edge on the coffee table close to his father. Touching his hands, he glanced at the letter locked in the old man's fist. "How do you feel?" Dan asked after a long silence.

"How should I feel? Like shit!" his father spat out, his lips curling tightly at the words.

Dan dropped his head into his hands and stared at the floor. There were times, and this morning was one of them, when Dan felt a deep sorrow that he had ever been born. The old man had always passed his responsibilities and feelings onto his son, and his blame for his wife's betrayal festered deep in Dan's soul. For years he had shouldered the guilt of his mother's actions and now, as he sat across from his father, there was a fearful struggle on Dan's features—a terrible struggle between love and hatred.

Dan loved his father and felt his sorrow and the fight to save his dignity, but he was constantly made to feel responsible for his mother's disappearance. As a young boy, he would often sit in deep thought, like now, trying to figure it all out—always blaming himself for not being able to restore his family's harmony.

"I am not sick." His father's words broke the pounding rhythm of Dan's thoughts. "You know I have no sickness... the only sickness I have is your mother and I've never been able to find a cure. I wish I had never laid eyes on her." He straightened himself up and yelled toward the kitchen door where Dan's grandmother made her way quietly. "It is your darling daughter that brought this sickness upon my children and me... It is your mother," he yelled, throwing the last words at Dan one more time.

"I know," Dan whispered, slowly nodding his head in agreement.

"No one knows how I feel. Everyone has left me. Everyone! Even you." The old man pointed his finger at Dan. "You are too busy for me. You have your own woman now." He clutched his chest with sorrow. "You have your own wife and soon you will be too busy to see me." He tightened his fingers around the paper. "They are all the same. I have not met a good, honest woman yet. Women are the curse of man. They are the roots of all misery. I watch you, my son. It is only the beginning for you. You have much to learn. Look at me; all I have left is a letter." He opened his fist and spread the paper in front of Dan. Still holding it tightly, he said, "This letter is from your mother."

"Let me see it," Dan said extending his hand to take the letter from his father "When did you receive it?"

His father drew away from him. "No," he shouted shoving the letter under his cushion.

"Why not?" Dan cried, raising his voice in frustration. "I'd like to see the letter. She may have been your wife but she is my mother." Dan was more demanding than ever and his voice took on a harshness that his father was not used to hearing.

"Easy boy. Don't you ever raise your voice around me! I am your father and I am still here. I did not leave you like your mother. Don't you be disrespectful toward me. I am your father."

Dan looked down like a little child ashamed of his mistake. His father got up from his seat, put his hand on Dan's shoulder and laughed loudly. "That's all right, my boy. I understand. She is your mother. She is 'the woman.' She is the one who causes the misery. You see what I mean?"

Dan felt like he was cut to half his size with that same uneasy feeling in his stomach that he had grown up with. It was like a constant gnawing. "I still want to see the letter," Dan said meekly. His bravado had slid out of him in the face of his father's anger.

"This is not the first letter I have ever received from her so don't be so excited. It is not even directly from her. She wrote to her brother in London and he mailed it to your aunt in Jerusalem who sent it to me. It does not even concern you, my boy. She doesn't really care about you. If she did, she would never have left in the first place. She wanted to be with her lover, not with you, my boy," he retorted shrugging his shoulders with some strange satisfaction.

"You never told me that we could communicate with

her," Dan said with his yearning for her apparent in his eyes. "Why didn't you ever tell me?" As his frustration settled, he slowly began to realize his even bigger loss, the loss of his father's trust and love. "The letter," Dan demanded again feeling some of his old anger returning.

"What's so important about the letter? She doesn't mention you at all," his old man shouted and shoved Dan's hand away. "She never wanted you anyway. She hated being pregnant! You were the first born, her first pregnancy, then your brothers and sister. She was too young, only fifteen years old, but she was my wife. I took care of her. I took good care of her and her mother. I still take care of her mother. I am stuck with old Naomi for the rest of my life."

Dan loved his grandmother. He saw his mother's love in her face. She was a gentle lady who submitted to his father's needs. She cooked, cleaned and raised his brothers and sister. She also desperately made sure to stay out of the way.

A cold sweat broke out all over Dan's body. The old man had laid everything bare. He had said it plainly, so very plainly, and the words hung in the air for a long time. Dan remained frozen in place, feeling as if all his courage had been drained from him. He felt as if his world was collapsing all around him. He felt himself caught up in a maelstrom of conflicting feelings.

Finally, he grasped at the letter and started reading. The old man did not interfere now. He only watched his son's eyes moving along as he read the words. He waited silently.

"There is not one single word about me!" Dan cried and threw the letter down. "Not one single rotten word about me. I don't believe it!" His voice faded as he stood glued in place.

"I told you. She doesn't care. Maybe she has forgotten she ever had you."

"So, I was never wanted. I have always been a person in the wrong circumstances. Is that it?"

"Yes," his father hit back at him. "That is your past. But now it is all right. Now, you are a grown man, a good man. Now, you are a public figure, a man of the world and no one should ever know our little secret. Now you have your own wife, your own woman. And you must learn how to handle her."

"So what if I've grown up!" Dan yelled. "Everyone grows up! So what if I have my own wife! Everyone has a wife! But I am inside here," he cried plaintively pointing at his heart, "and inside here there is nothing. I am nothing! I feel nothing. You must know it well, Father," and he started laughing harshly.

"Everything started with your crazy mother," his father cried back shrilly. "I tell you, women are the root of all misery." Anticipating Dan's agreement, he continued with renewed strength. "Women are nothing… yet they have the power to drag us down. They wind us around their little fingers. Look at your own mother," he continued. "Look at what she has done to all of us," and he spread his hands around the room. "Look at your own grandmother. How she kept those secrets from me the whole time her daughter was screwing around."

"And now what? What do you want me to do?" Dan asked.

"Nothing, my boy. Everything has been done by now! You read the letter."

"I know. It said in the letter that she is going to be in London next week."

"Yes, but what the hell do I care," Dan's father continued to shout. "She will be there with her lover, her new husband, your stepfather!" He laughed loudly at the mere idea of it all. "I did not want you to see the letter. It is not good for you." He bent down and picked the letter up off the floor. "You see, it means nothing," and he tore it into little pieces. He flung them up in the air in front of Dan's face.

"I hate her!" Dan shouted, twisting his face, "I hate women! And yes, I understand! You don't care… you haven't cared for a long time. But, maybe I care. Did you ever think about that?"

"No, you can't care for her! She did not care for you, remember?" There was a bit of fear in his father's voice. "I turned you into a great man. You can't leave me. You can't go to her now."

"No, I am not leaving you but I need to tell you that I am tired of all this drama. I need to live my own life. I need some peace."

"I know that," his father said softly with a look of compassion on his face.

Dan could not recall many times in his life that his father had said kind and gentle words to him. All his life he had yearned for it, and now, it was almost too late. Dan couldn't feel anything. He walked across the room bereft.
"I have to go now. I don't want any part of my past anymore. If only I could leave my past behind." Dan spoke softly, as if he was speaking to himself. He walked out of the room slamming the door behind him and leaving the old man in astonishment at his sudden departure.

Later on, Dan chided himself for his lack of patience and self-control. True, that morning he had left his father's home claiming some of his dignity and his right for a life of his own, but he took with him also strong feelings of rejection, self-doubt and worthlessness. Those feelings were all too familiar to him. Although his father's compulsive thought stayed with him all afternoon, he kept looking for a tiny ray of sunshine, something to give him hope.

In the evening, he returned home with a wide smile on his face and carrying a basket of orchids in his arms. "My father's flu is over. The old man passed it on to me." He laughed at his own joke and pulling me close to him, he gently slid me toward the bedroom. "I want to make love to you, my Sara. I was thinking about you all afternoon. I couldn't do anything else." He held me with both hands now. "Give me one more chance," he said softly and I followed him faithfully into the other room.

He pressed his body to mine and I felt the hardness of his penis against me. He seemed eager, almost impatiently so, as if trying to find relief. He moved quickly and turned the light off. "It is better this way," he said as he started to take his clothes off. I could see the outline of his body in the cool light of the evening. The bedroom window was open and a calming light filled the room. He was completely naked when he joined me on the bed stretching his body next to mine.

I was still a virgin and I sensed Dan was wrapped up in his struggle to perform. "Take your clothes off," he directed impatiently after making an awkward attempt to unbutton my blouse. Reluctantly, I undressed myself wondering all the while if we couldn't do this with a little more romance. This awkward passion felt uncomfortable and I wanted to be made love to. Dan, however, was rushing his touch. His hands caressed my body nervously, eager to fulfill his needs. He was breathing heavily and his body began to perspire. I tried to let go. Instead, I found myself feeling frustrated and anxious. I could not seem to abandon myself to his nervousness. I remained silent and was sorry to feel Dan's body dropping beside me in distress. "I am useless. I am just useless," he said in his disappointment.

"Don't say that," I whispered.

He lay there silently. I could feel the cold stillness of his core as if his life was seeping away. We were lying next to each other but the distance between us was greater than ever before. I did not know how to breach the gap nor did I know what was expected of me. We were totally exposed in our powerlessness. Strange how I felt responsible for Dan's inability to perform.

CHAPTER 11

My Essence

Saying no can be the ultimate self-care.
—Claudia Black

The next few days I felt sluggish and full of apprehension. It felt like I had to be careful of what I did or said. Most of Dan's communication with me was defensive. One morning as we both were getting ready to leave for work, he looked at me and said, "You know, you really do look like a teacher. You have that perfect image. Just be careful never to teach your students about a man like me."

"Don't think like that," I said, annoyed.

"Oh, now you are going to tell me how to think, too," he retorted. "Well, you can tell them about yourself then: beautiful, strong, risen from poverty to greatness."

"Greatness?!" I was surprised.

"Yes, greatness. Don't you think being the wife of the great Dan Tavor is achieving greatness?!" he sarcastically asked. I was confused but quiet, not daring to challenge his remark. Raising my head, I looked at him puzzled. "I hate it when you look at me like that," he continued, as he walked toward the door intending to go to his editorial office.

"Like what?" I impatiently provoked him.

"Like you pity me… Don't pity me. I am not dead yet!"

"What are you talking about?" I cried, raising my voice to him. He reminded me of my father with his unspoken anger and blame. I always had to guess what he was thinking and what I could have possibly done wrong. Then, I had to figure out how I could fix it. As I looked at Dan, the years slid away and I felt like that little girl again.

I had wanted to have Dan as a friend. I cherished the thought that he might one day be the closest person to me. I was learning, however, that I was extremely naïve about life and relationships. My knowledge about how to build a good marriage was next to nothing. I did not like what I had learned from my parents and, in fact, I tried very hard not to repeat their mistakes. Naively, I believed that if I was a good, honest, and open person, I would get that back. The shock of finding out that I was dead wrong hurt me. He was not interested in a friendship with me. I believe that the thought that I might become his equal had never crossed his mind. I was his wife and he was my husband. That was it… Interesting, I thought, that the word husband in Hebrew is "Baal" which means owner. Now, it became clear to me that all Dan wanted at this point was to claim his ownership of me. His ego had been bruised by our earlier interactions and now he wanted to restore his manhood in whatever way he could.

"Don't ask me what I am talking about," he retorted. He turned back and started walking toward me. "You know what I am talking about. Ever since that night when

I couldn't perform, when I could not satisfy you, you have been walking around here depressed and cold. You hardly talk to me. You know, I was not the only one in bed. You were there too, not helping at all…" He waited for my reaction.

"I am not blaming you," I finally uttered.

"So why are you so silent?"

"I am afraid to say the wrong thing," I replied. "In fact, I don't talk at all because I don't want to upset you."

"Upset me? Well, why don't you say something good then?"

"Okay, let's talk now," I said, reaching for his hands but he pulled away from me with a cold look.

"What do you want now?" he asked sharply, and with one single question I was put on the defensive.

A part of me wanted to just pull back again and go quiet. Instead, I gathered myself together and said with an intelligent expression, "I'd like to explain to you why I have not been speaking much. It is because I am afraid to say the wrong thing. That one night did not mean so much to me but every time it comes up you get so angry. I just want to tell you it was no big deal. It was not that important."

"You don't know what you're talking about. What do you mean that it was not important?!"

"Wait, before you get angry again. I mean it. It is okay with me not to have sex right away. There's no rush. You and me—that's what really matters to me."

I think he was surprised to hear me speaking up with some confidence even if it was based on ignorance. In reality, I was weary about all the talking and planning about our lovemaking. To this day I am not sure I can figure out the state I was in after *that night*. I became numb inside and my heart felt like it continued to beat only out of habit. The romance, the love, the tenderness felt shattered and I hid behind my veneer of confidence to avoid a confrontation.

Finally, I think he heard me and I saw his face becoming softer. He moved closer to me and with some hesitation he hugged me. I heard his heavy breathing slowly becoming restful and calm. We stayed there for a long moment. Finally, he brushed his hair with his long fingers as if he was taking a second look at the situation, considering all the facts, and trying to gain some confidence with me. Then he wrapped his arms around my body again and we rested in each other's arms. It was a beautiful feeling of coming home.

"Come, sit here with me," he murmured and pulling me gently toward the sofa, he placed me on his lap. "Tell me, tell me everything you feel. What do you truly think about me? Tell me something good. I need to hear it from you. I love you so much." His words poured out of his mouth very fast and his eyes kept searching mine. I felt overwhelmed and a little bit uncomfortable as he, all of a sudden, gave me so much power over him. I held his face in my hands and buried his face gently in my chest.

"I love you, too," I said, loving the fact that he dared to open up and risk his ego with me.

"It sure took you a long time to say that," he whispered and kissed me lightly on my lips. It was as if he was almost grateful. "So, you really are okay with me?" He pulled away and looked straight into my eyes for reassurance.

"Yes, I am," and I nodded my head in agreement.

"You are my beautiful virgin wife. You know, the irony is that I got what I asked for and now I don't know what to do with it." He laughed as if to himself. He had a child-like expression on his face. His cheeks softened and I noticed his narrow lips become fuller as they dropped in a relaxed manner. I stroked his forehead and smoothed my palm over his dark thick hair. It felt so good to be accept-ed, so good to taste intimate contact, so good for us both to be in this egoless space. How I longed for this all of the time-to just be, without demand and expectation.

"I love your hair," I said in a dreamy voice after a long moment of contentment. "I wish I had straight silky hair like yours. You know I hate my curls."

"Ah, yes, your curls… do you have a problem with your curls?"

"I've always hated them—my frizzy curls. Do you like them?"

"I like them," he smiled. "I'll bet you would look beau-tiful in very short hair. Like a boy's haircut. It would frame your face like a picture." Looking at his watch, he moved slowly. "I wish I could stay with you like this for the rest of the day but I have to go to work."

"So, do you want me to cut my hair?" I asked playfully.

"So, do you love me?" he countered.

We both giggled at our insecurity. We had such a com-mon need to be loved and accepted. If we were only able to see it and give it to each other rather than fear it and shield ourselves so often from the hurt.

"So, you are sure you are okay with me?" he asked again. "I will make it up to you."

"Sure I am okay. I don't know what it is anyway. I never made love before." I laughed and felt in such good spirits. We embraced and Dan left for work, both of us once more feeling comfortable with each other.

I thought of the talk I had had with my Grandmother
Sophie the night before my wedding. She took me by the
hand and very seriously sat me down. She began by
smoothing her hand over her cotton dress and looking at
me with a kind smile. I think she was the kind of woman
who let me get as close to her as I let her. She was never
moody or withdrawn but always the one tenderhearted
person in my life. She understood the child in me and
respected the woman I was becoming. I loved her for that.
I loved her full round figure and her easy ways. I loved her
white thinning hair and her rosy cheeks. And most of all,
I loved her beautiful smile which carried so much wisdom
in its twinkle.

"Come here, my child," she began. "Sit closer to me.
Do you know what I want to talk about?"

"No," I said staring at her earnestly.

"Well, this is not comfortable for me but I need to ask
you this," and she put her arm around my shoulder. "Tell
me, my dear child… are you still a virgin?"

"Yes, I am," I said with a slight blush crossing my face.

"Of course. I should not even ask."

But I could tell she was pleased. "So," she continued,
"you see this is going to be very important to your husband. Tomorrow night is a very important night. When
your husband takes you to the wedding bed, he will want
proof—of your virginity. It is our custom to have a white
sheet handy to show the stain of your virginity. It is very
important that your husband will have no doubt that he is
the first man and the only man to know you." She paused
and placing my palm in her hand asked softly, "Do you
understand?"

I nodded my head knowing that I was absolutely will-

ing to go along with this custom. I didn't see any harm in
it. In fact, it gave the wedding night a sacred feeling. I was
filled with questions like how does a woman know love
and what keeps it alive, but she kept on talking in her low,
gentle voice. "It is also very important to keep the white
sheet with your virginity stain as sometimes the husband's
family will ask for it as proof. This is your honor and the
honor of our family that you are untouched by a man
before your wedding night."

"I understand," I said seriously.

She gently leaned forward and kissed my forehead,
smoothing her hand over my hair with kindness. "It is all
good," she told me with confidence. "It is all good. You
will see."

Now I sat on the edge of the sofa in our living room
reflecting on my honeymoon and my very first physical
encounter with my husband. All of the eagerness of my
almost nineteen years was circling around in my body. I sat
holding my head in both hands smiling to myself. I touched
my forehead lightly wishing to bring back that precious
moment when my grandma had kissed me with her
approval and acceptance. In her gentle way she had been
asking me to carry the responsibility of clearing the honor
and respect of the entire family. It was as if she had been
sending me on a mission. And what a strange situation I was
in now. I smiled again thinking of the irony. Three weeks
after my wedding night and still a virgin.

But, finally it happened. After riding a seesaw of emotions back and forth between the two of us, one night in
the dark under a light blanket Dan penetrated me and I
officially became a woman. I had the white sheet close by
and I was able to redeem my family and prove my honor.

It all took less than a few moments. As I recall, I didn't feel any ecstasy nor did I see any fireworks. In any case, the task was fulfilled. Dan was content and I could finally breathe a sigh of relief. But, there was a part of me that still felt overwhelmed by the unknown. True, I had physically experienced the act of sex but there must be more to making love than this. Inside, that little voice was whispering louder than all the others, overwhelming even the screaming of my culture and its conditioning.

What I felt inside my body and soul was quite different from what I could reveal on the outside. Inside I was bewildered and alone. There was a mix of wonder and loss— wonder that I had finally become a "woman" and loss for the fairy tale dream I had nurtured for so long. Outwardly, I seemed calm and collected, still wearing the glamorous and alluring dresses Dan continued to order for me.

But the more I denied my true hunger for love and acceptance, the more it manifested itself. Although I was able to hide it from most, those with a penetrating eye could read me pretty well. I believe it was very clear to men, especially to the men in our social circle, Dan's friends. They could see the unsettling dynamic that played back and forth between Dan and me. Learning about life in the big city was new to me. Learning about other people's motives and behaviors was new; the politics of life and the business of love were new. In this world I felt lost. Dan was my husband and I wanted to find assurance and shelter in him but Dan seemed to have a different idea. His priority seemed to be the maintaining of his ego. Showing me off was one way to enhance his self-image and to gain his own sense of confidence. I could not make sense of his desire to dress me up in quite revealing and sensuous outfits as if he was displaying me for the pleasure of everyone. It seemed as if he was offering me to them. It felt uncomfortable to me and I felt a sense of abandonment.

Looking back, I feel a tremendous sense of sorrow. I forgot my inner voice and myself for years. I refrained from trusting my own gut and coming to my own rescue. I failed to let my inner voice speak out for years after Dan's death. I know now that everything I did and every word I uttered was rooted in my need to be "a good girl." But was the price I paid too high?

CHAPTER 12

The Desert Flower

An eye for an eye makes the whole world blind.
—Mahatma Gandhi

It was early June 1967, and a heavy tension hung in the air. One more time, Israel was facing the dangers of being hacked to pieces and pushed to the sea. Day by day the conflict increased and the concern of possible war was very real.

Dan was extremely busy. He spent many hours at army offices in Kiryah in Tel Aviv as well as at his office at the newspaper. One evening I went to visit him at his editorial office. His door was wide open and the sound of an Arabic broadcast filtered loudly through the rooms. I watched him silently from the doorframe of his office.

He was sitting in front of his desk, his head lowered, and his jaw set. His right hand was leaning against his head and with his left he was smoothing his dark thin mustache, examining and reexamining the paper in his typewriter. As the baritone voice of the Arabic announcer crackled through the radio, Dan ripped the paper out of the type-writer and crushed it in both his hands. It took a long minute for him to notice me as he was in deep thought. "Ah, come in, my dearest wife… I'm so glad to see you. You're like a breeze of fresh air, like a beautiful flower," he said in poetic Arabic and got up to hug me.

"You spoke to me in Arabic," I said in surprise.

"Yes, the Arabic language is a most romantic and beau-tifully poetic language. You are my flower," he said again in a deep Arabic voice. "My flower of the desert," he mur-mured looking straight into my eyes. "Did you know that? Did you know you're a flower of the desert—strong and beautiful? You are a survivor… you will survive everything like the desert flower. Nothing will crush it. Not the siz-zling sun, not the hated wind or the sand. Nothing will take its beauty!" He laughed and raised his hand with an excla-mation. "You are strong and beautiful just like the desert flower," he concluded, pausing as if waiting for my reaction. I laughed loudly with obvious pleasure. I liked his spirit and enjoyed the compliment.

Still, watching Dan speak with so much vigor and authority, I was surprised to say the least. Where did he get this notion that I was strong and beautiful? He glanced at me, noticing my doubt and added, "It is true. You are a strong woman, a survivor! You will survive me. I have no doubt of it!" he concluded. "You know that, don't you?"

Taking a deep breath, he switched his attention to his work. "Sometimes, I have this fantasy," he said, smiling at me with renewed spirit. "Imagine this," he said to me in a wistful tone. Dan used to often repeat in order to make sure he was clearly heard. "Imagine this… if we could possibly achieve a real peace with our neighbors, the Arabs. I mean a real peace, where we could collaborate and join as one force. Where we could help each other to build and grow, hand in hand… I mean a real peace with a warm heart not a cold and distant one. We with our technology and knowledge and them with their resources. The Middle East could truly become the richest place on the face of the earth." He paused and sank his body into the chair behind his desk.

For a moment he was silent. "But, of course, I am only dreaming. Listen to them," and he turned the volume of the Arabic station louder. The voice was full of hatred and its usual passion to push Israel to the sea. The announcer spoke about the need and desire of every Arab to crush Israel.

"How can we ever turn this hate into love and kindness?" He shook his head with disappointment and continued. "I know it is a dream. Their hate is real and I can't underestimate it. I really think that war is near," he said sadly. "This is not the first time that they are after us and it will not be the last."

Silently, I agreed with Dan. I, too, felt vulnerable. It was such a helpless situation. Slowly, I started walking around Dan's office. I stopped by a large plant that he had earlier removed from the corner and saw that it was back in its original place. He saw me looking at it and smiled. "I thought it was only right to include this plant in my life. Who knows, it might even outlive me…"

"Why do you talk like that?" I interrupted.

"You always ask me that. I talk as I wish to talk." He made his point very clearly and continued. "Anything is possible. Besides, I think that one has to choose his time. One has to know when to exit. It is our right you know." He did not wait for my reaction but went back to his writing. From time to time he would glance up from his desk filled with paper clips, books and Teleprinter slips.

"I have to write one more news item and then we can go to dinner. Where do you want to eat?" He lifted up his head answering his own question. "I would love to go to Schunnat Hatikva. I feel like having some kebab."

"Sure, I will come with you but I'm not sure I can eat anything. I have an upset stomach. I'll wait for you in the lobby," I said.

"No, stay here. I love your presence."

Feeling special and important, I smiled and sat on the edge of the chair in front of Dan.

We left the editorial office shortly afterward and took a taxi to Schunnat Hatikva, Dan's favorite little town adjacent to Tel Aviv. He had grown up there. It was mostly populated by Jews who had immigrated to Israel from Iraq in 1951. In the main street there was a small restaurant that served Middle Eastern food. The food was always fresh and cooked right there in a small kitchen in the back. Very often, the cook would be the owner's wife. She would come out and make sure that you liked the meat that was to be cooked. Dan loved the intimate atmosphere. When his family had migrated from Baghdad, Dan was 11 years of age and much of the tradition and way of life was still fresh and vivid in his memory. He used to speak of it with nostalgia.

This particular evening, Dan was especially happy to be here. Most everyone in the restaurant knew who he was and he always got special treatment and service. In the background there was Arabic music playing. Dan took a sip from the hot Turkish coffee, which they had placed in front of him when we sat down.

"So, how is my beautiful teacher?" He spoke softly with the tiniest touch of sarcasm. "How are your students these

days? Do they love their teacher? How can they help it?"
He kept on talking as if I was not there. "And your students,
how old are they? Ah, old enough to love you. I'll bet you
they don't remember a thing you teach them because
they're all just staring at their beautiful teacher." After a
moment he continued, "Just don't confuse yourself and
think for a second that I am your student as well." Although
he smiled, there was an edge in his voice.

He continued drinking his coffee and casually added, "It
looks like I will have to leave tomorrow for a few days."

"Where to?" I asked.

Before Dan could answer my question the waiter was
in front of our table, ready to take our order. "The usual,
Sami. With extra hot pepper… and put the pita on the fire,"
Dan ordered for both of us.

Sami nodded his head in satisfaction. "It is good to see
you again, Mr. Tavor. It is always a pleasure." He turned and
made his way back to the kitchen.

"Where are you going, Dan?" I asked again.

"Turkey," he said and examined my face.

"Turkey?"

"A press conference," he said absentmindedly.

"It seems a strange place for a press conference," I said.

"Why not Turkey? Where would you want a press conference to happen?" I could sense he was impatient with
me.

"Geneva is a better place," I shrugged.

"Oh, come on, Sara. Turkey is fine. I am leaving tomorrow morning and before you know it I will be back."

"Tomorrow? Just like that. Why did you wait so long
to tell me?"

"Because I did not know myself. You know this is the

type of work I do," he snapped. We sat in silence until the food arrived. Sami placed the warm pita close to Dan's plate the way he liked it and the kebab was hot and steamy as ordered.

"I will call you," he said quietly. "You know that." He pulled the pita in half with his hand and put one half on my plate while he took a bite from the other. With a full mouth he added, "I asked my friend, Yoel, to give you a call just to see if you need anything."

"You shouldn't do that," I responded and stopped eating. "It's really not necessary… I told you what happened the last time you asked Yoel to be in touch with me while you were abroad."

"That was sheer nonsense," he snapped, dismissing my intimation.

"You don't believe me?"

"Of course I believe you… you're a beautiful woman. What did you expect?"

"Come on, Dan. He made a pass at me and he is your friend!"

"You're making a big deal of it," Dan replied, continuing to eat his food.

"He made a pass at me," I repeated, and opened my eyes wide in disbelief. "Don't you care? Don't you mind?" I asked indignantly.

"You have a strong imagination," he muttered.

"I don't believe you… what are you saying?" I lowered my voice and closed my eyes with shame. It seemed strange that he would so lightly dismiss my concern. And why would he think that I might make up such a story anyway? I did not know what to make of it. I felt alone and unprotected and I could not ignore the feeling in my stomach. I looked into his big brown almond-shaped eyes that were fringed with long lashes. Then I moved my glance to his mouth. He was chewing with enjoyment and pleasure totally oblivious to my feelings and concern. I felt totally invalidated. I felt very much on my own.

I could not help going back to Yoel's visit at our home when Dan was abroad last time. His soft, seductive words rang in my head now: "Let me love you like a man should love you and protect you." I dared to look straight into Dan's eyes now and wonder about his behavior, still feeling alone.

"Why are you staring at me like that?" He stopped chewing for a short while and moved his hand to encourage me. "Go ahead. Eat."

"I can't. I told you. I have an upset stomach," I said.

Fortunately, a further answer was not needed at that moment. It was as if heaven intervened. The harsh deafening noise of Mirage Airplanes and Air Force jets flew above us followed by a broken alert. It was a clear warning for danger. There was no doubt we were in a war zone.

People in the restaurant threw worried looks at each other. While swallowing his last bite, Dan motioned for the check and hurriedly threw a large bill on the table. We left at once and made our way to our car where I slid in behind the wheel.

The city of Tel Aviv was almost empty of men. Most males over 18 years of age had been drafted. Only women, older people and children populated the city. The heavy traffic slowed down and the bright lights turned off amid a deep tension in the air. "Let's go to my editorial office," Dan muttered. I drove as fast as I could but suddenly a loud alert cut through the air. It felt like a sharp knife slicing through my insides. I stopped the car at once and held onto the wheel. "Don't stop," Dan ordered.

"But the alert… We should go to a shelter," I cried anxiously.

"No… keep on going! I need to be at the Kiryah!" he shouted. I turned the car's parking lights to dim and drove on carefully. Finally, we reached the Kiryah, the seat of the Government and Army offices in Tel Aviv. Dan jumped out of the car and said, "Go home and stay there. I will call you." He squeezed my hand out of the car window and gave me a light kiss on my cheek. "Go, I will call you."

I pressed down on the gas pedal and took a sharp turn. By this time, the road was wide open and empty of cars and I was home within a few minutes. It was the longest Sunday night of my life. The news was not clear—the Israeli radio and TV did not reveal very much. The Israeli stations played music throughout the night and did not offer any information that the enemy could use. The next morning the world awakened to the first day of the "Six Days War."

I did not hear from Dan that night and I did not see him for the next few days. Tuesday morning he called from the Israeli Air Force Center in the south of the country. "We knocked off most of the Egyptian force and we now have the upper hand!" Dan's voice was strong and confident but I didn't learn very much. I learned more about his activities from his articles in the newspaper. Those were reassuring messages that he was still alive and functioning.

For the next few days I sat suspended near the phone and the radio. I didn't obey the alerts nor did I go down to the shelter. Dan had written in one of his articles, "We need a few more miracles. Our men are fighting like heroes." And there was a picture of Dan with a group of

soldiers at the top of the page. The veil of smoke and dust
could not hide their happiness. There was no chance that
the Egyptian army would be able to wipe Israel off the face
of the map. Filled with emotion, I hugged the paper to my
heart. The next time I heard from Dan it was Friday morning at ten minutes to five. He raised his voice as much as he
could, but I could hardly put his words together. The whis-
tles from gunfire and the battle cries in the background
were far stronger than Dan's voice. The fighting that was
raging on in Jerusalem was from rooftop to rooftop, room
to room, hand to hand.

"This holy place of all religions should not be damaged.
The blood here is flowing like a river... I can't bear it... it
is too miserable... the young are dying like..." Dan's voice
was hoarse. "I can't talk long. I am fine though... you take
care of yourself. I can't stop thinking about you. I want you
to be safe and ready for me when I get back... I want you
to go to the doctor and tell him you are not feeling well.
Maybe it is strange to be thinking of such things in the
middle of a war zone, but I am hoping maybe the sickness
is a sign of something. It has been going on for a couple of
weeks and I need to know. I so hope I am right... I love..."

Amid the shouting and the bullets whizzing by, we
were disconnected. I replaced the receiver slowly on its
cradle and thought of this man who was my husband. A
mix of love and fear flooded my heart. In the midst of war
where death was unavoidable and distraction was everywhere, Dan was right to hope for a new birth, a new life.
As for myself, I wasn't sure about anything except for the
fact that I didn't want to disappoint Dan.

Dan returned to Tel Aviv a few days later and by that
time the war was over. In the days following his return, he

tried to relax and write his commentaries from home. He was quiet and introspective. Frequently, he was prey to ugly moods. Most of the time, he kept to himself and it was very hard to approach him. He complained of a headache but refused to take anything for it. He mostly walked around with his head down and his hands clasped together appearing deep in thought and very troubled. It was as if he was wearing a mask.

Sometimes in the middle of the night he would slide his body away from me and sit on the edge of the bed. I could not help but feel his energy and his distress as I watched him bend down like an old man with a heavy weight on his shoulders. One morning I extended my arm toward him and touched his back lightly. He turned toward me. "Go back to sleep. It is too early for you," he said in a gloomy voice.

"It is okay. I want to be with you."

"You will not understand. Go back to sleep. You need your beauty rest," he concluded and stood up.

"Are you angry with me?" I inquired looking at him standing tall. The cool morning light outlined his figure. His chest was bare and his pajama bottoms hugged his lower torso very loosely. The early morning sun was already shining through the windowpane and its rays illuminated Dan's soft hair. I looked at him silently. His face was somber and his eyes avoided mine. Silently, he brushed his long fingers through his hair.

"No, I am not angry with you. How could I be angry with you? I am angry about the injustice that…" He stopped short.

"Tell me what you mean?" I said sitting up and wrapping my arms around my knees.

"Tell you what? What do you think I know that you don't?" Suddenly, a look of impatience crossed his face and he took a deep breath. "I was hoping that our soldiers would reach Baghdad!" He stopped and looked at me.

"Baghdad?" I was amazed.

"Yes, Baghdad!" he said, nodding his head with certainty. "I really wanted that."

"Are you joking? Who needs Baghdad? Don't we have enough enemies?" I said with a half smile.

"Personally, I need Baghdad," retorted Dan. "Just for an hour or so. I have a long-standing account to square with one of its inhabitants."

I sat silently, not sure what to say. The sun snaked in through the shutters and I could see Dan's face very clearly now. There was a deep unexplained pain engraved in his expression. His eyebrows knit close together and almost became one. His lips were tight and his cheeks seemed longer and thinner than ever before. He was still standing in one place and I could feel his anxiety. I slid off the bed and stood by him. Holding his hand, I pulled him gently back toward the bed.

"Come, sit here with me," I said.

He pushed my hand away and seated me back on the bed again. "You sit. I'm okay here. I can't sit right now," and he nodded his head with disappointment. "I just wish we had gotten to Baghdad," he said again as if speaking to himself.

"Why?" I could not help asking again.

He waved his hand and laughed—a harsh, bitter laugh. Seeing that I didn't understand him, he extended his hand to me with moist, sweaty fingers. There fell a heavy silence and for a short time Dan seemed to search for the right words. His face became stiff and hard and he watched me intently. Finally, he broke the silence.

"I would like to get to Baghdad to take revenge on someone, a very significant someone to me. I want to spill her blood," he hissed. "I want to ask her if she recognizes me. 'I'm your beloved firstborn son,' I would tell her and then I'd shoot her in the face. I'd spoil her makeup and watch her fall. I'd kick her when she was down and then I'd tell her to get out of my life for good!" His hands gestured wildly as he spoke and his lips closed on the words very fast. He shouted as if he wanted her to hear him. He stalked the room and kicked the armchair. As he started to calm down, he sent a quick glance toward me and added, "After that, we can forget about Baghdad for all I care. You're absolutely right—who needs more enemies?" Finally, he walked toward me and sat on the edge of the bed as if he had finished his outburst. He started moving his feet with nervousness back and forth. I took his hand in mine and looked at him with compassion, not knowing what to say or do.

"Don't look at me like that," he spat out. "Stop pitying me. I hate that look of yours that says I am less than!" He covered his face with his hands in shame and I could hear his silent weeping. I sat as though stoned, unable to say or do anything. I longed to speak to him but my words would not come out. I was afraid of his reaction; I was concerned that my words would be misinterpreted. In silence, I watched his pain, his hatred and his anger. After a few minutes, the heavy silence felt like it was cutting the air. I could not be passive anymore and so I slid slowly across the bed until I was close to him and extended my arms to hug him, to bring his shivering body close to mine. I held him near and whispered his name. I wanted us to become one at that moment. I wanted to feel that intimacy of caring and embracing no matter what life brings. Together was better than alone, and I wanted him to know that he was not alone anymore, but all I could utter was, "Dan…"

He pushed me away. "Stop that! I told you not to pity me!" There was a deliberate firmness to his words. I felt ineffective and hated myself for being useless. I couldn't hide my surprise, however. He had always told me that his mother had died when he was eleven years old. "I lied to you. I lied to you all that time," he forced out. There were tears in his eyes but he managed to push them back.

"It's okay," I said quietly.

"No, it is not. I lied to you because I am ashamed of my past. I can't help it."

"I understand," I said.

"No you don't understand. How can you? Your mother…" he started but then held his words back.

"My mother left me, too," I reminded him. "I really do understand." I wanted so much to reassure him.

"But I don't see you hating your mother the way I hate mine."

"No, I don't hate her. But I understand the shame," I said softly. He lowered his face like a child and sat down on the side of the bed

I realized in that moment that we both were consumed by shame. I could see and understand Dan being fixated with his feelings of guilt and disgrace as I had felt sometimes in the past. His body slumped over and all I could see was the crown of his head with its beautiful dark and smooth hair. It was overwhelming to see how this feeling of shame took over his whole body and he became hostage to it. It was as if he was wrapped up within a dark, heavy cloud, disappearing into nowhere. I sat beside him feeling bare and exposed to his emotion.

I wondered what this force was that we call shame. Where did it come from? Who gave it the authority to take charge and change the life force within us, to alter the very breath we take? As Dan continued to weep silently, I wondered if this shame was a creation of society, planted in us by the people we admire the most. It definitely felt like a burden, a life sentence, a punishment handed down by those we love. I felt a flash of anger surge within me. In time I came to realize that shame itself is totally powerless and harmless unless we feed it and give it strength. Unless we give it permission to rule us. Unless we open our heart to it and allow it to enter our body and our soul. Only then, does it take on a life of its own. But, it would be many years before I myself fully realized that. I would have to struggle with my own demons and Dan's suicide before I would fully come to terms with this understanding. In the meantime, Dan embraced his shame as if it was a friend and confidant.

His muttering interrupted my thoughts. "I don't care anymore. No one cares about me anyway. I don't even care," he said in despair. "Since I have told you that I am not an orphan and I want to blow my mother's brains out, there is nothing left to hide. There is no image left to maintain." He was biting his lower lip fiercely. "I am tired of wars and struggle. I need some peace. I have this personal war inside my head that won't let me forget her—my mother—what a strange word. It is hard for me to say it. How much power this bloody word contains! I hate her for leaving me and my brothers and sister. I want her to pay. Is that so bad?" He raised up his hand and pointed his fingers as if they were a gun. Then he made the loud sound of a bullet. "That's what I want to do. Don't you see?" He dropped his hands to his sides as if he had lost all of his energy.

Talking to me in a softer, quieter voice as one would speak to a little child, he went on to explain, "You see, it is my duty to save the honor of my family. After all, I am the firstborn male."

"Duty?!" I could not help my astonishment. He was a mirror of myself. We both seemed ruled by our duty to save the family's honor.

"Yes, of course, it is my duty. Don't you understand? My mother stained our family's honor, especially my poor father's. She played her game expertly. She immigrated with us to Israel. She came with us all the way from Baghdad to Jerusalem and then, after a short while, she left and returned to her lover in Baghdad. She did not care about her husband or her children. She went back to her Muslim lover and lived happily ever after." He stopped short.

"But why did you always say that she was dead?" I asked.

"Well, of course, we declared her dead. What did you expect?" he wondered aloud and continued. "Since I technically became an orphan so long ago, I would like to vindicate myself now and become one for real." He liked the concept and sat rocking himself back and forth.

"I understand," I said quickly trying to ease the situation yet feeling further and further away from this man who was my husband.

"No you don't. How can you possibly understand? I have lived a lie all my life. I hate her with a passion!"

Suddenly, he dragged his body to the center of the bed

and stared at me with penetrating eyes. His hands started to pull at my nightgown. Drawing his fingers over the lace, he pushed his hand to touch my breast. I moved away feeling uncomfortable. "Come here, baby; make love to me." His voice was throaty and demanding. Quietly, feeling myself frosting over from the inside out, I pulled away and with a forced smile I said, "No, not now."

"No?" he repeated with surprise.

"Well... I don't think..."

"Well what? Come here, my little woman," he said pulling me by the nightgown firmly with impatience. He drew the long fingers of one hand through my hair and rested his other hand on my chin. "You know," he said as he brought his face closer to mine "you remind me of my mother. You look a lot like her: the shape of your face, your smooth dark skin, your curls and your smile. You resemble her in many ways." His eyes dropped down to my body as he grabbed me by the neck and kissed me strongly. I tried to free myself but he held on tightly. After a long deep kiss, he released me and pushed me roughly down onto the bed.

"Dan, please stop," I gasped. "Not now, please."

"Even the tone of your voice... you sound like her," he said ignoring my wish. "It is unbelievable. You who I love the most," he said with harsh laughter. "Oh yes, she was also very beautiful, very sexy, just like you. I remember her very well."

I composed myself slowly and carefully moved away while pulling the bed sheet as a cover, not sure what to expect. But he kept on speaking as if he was reading a story.

"Men followed her and wanted her. Men could smell her sexuality and she wanted them as much as they wanted her. It was this silent communication. She really didn't love my father. The poor old man gave her everything she wanted but that wasn't enough for her! So she lied and took what she wanted. She was such a bitch," he concluded and looked at me as though daring me to disagree.

"But you don't have to be afraid of me, Sara. I love you," and he pointed at me with his finger while putting a special emphasis on the word 'you.' "You, too, are beautiful and sexy. No wonder men want you. Tell me about Yoel. Did you make love to him? Tell me," he demanded.

"No," I cried.

"I know he wanted you. Why not? I want you, too," and he dragged his body over next to me, pulling me closer to him and grabbing onto my nightgown forcing it down. I heard the tear of the lace and my naked body shivered under his hands as he ripped his pajama pants off and threw his entire body over mine. "You are my wife, you belong to me body and soul. I own you and you will do what I tell you to do." His voice was shaky and laden with heavy breathing. I shut my eyes and remained still swallowing my pain and choking on my tears. It took only a short moment but it felt to me like an eternity. My body was tight and cold and my heart became still. I held my breath and waited for him to let go of me. Finally, he slid off my body and lay on his back breathing with a sense of relief. I carefully rolled off the bed, still holding onto the bed sheet and stumbled toward the shower.

Once inside, I slowly turned on the water. My body felt numb. I desperately wanted to wash away my humiliation but there was not enough water to do so.

CHAPTER 13

Point of View

I am not bound to please thee with my answers.
—William Shakespeare

A few days later I met Dan for an afternoon snack in a small coffee shop at the end of Iben-Gevirol Street. We used to meet there frequently and Dan would order his usual milk shake with extra whipped cream on the side, and I would have my Turkish coffee and pull out my cigarette with a sense of importance. Dan used to take the lighter out of my hand and lean close to me with an obvious gentleman's gesture and light my cigarette, but today he didn't even bother. He just watched me with a smile on his face— absorbing the 'Sara' he had created. *I guess like all other gods he had to watch and estimate his work*, I thought bitterly. What was funny, however, was that even though he hardly smoked, he had encouraged me to take up the habit and I had willingly adapted.

Lately, Dan had made sure to invite a friend or two to join us at the coffee shop. It was as though we were both making sure to have people around us in order to avoid confronting our life face to face. Especially at night I would always make sure to invite someone over for dinner, or Dan would show up with one of his friends from the office, usually Barak and his wife, Debbie, who were newlyweds. They did not seem to have the tension between them that Dan and I had. Debbie was outspoken and sure of herself. She appeared to know what she wanted and she had no problems asking for it. Barak, a heavyset man with a round face and an easy, gentle manner was always ready to tell a joke or two and keep the conversation light. He and Dan had worked hand in hand on the Israeli/Arab affair and were always in close touch. So we were glad to have them join us and take the heavy feeling away.

This afternoon, however, Dan and I sat alone in the coffee shop, each quietly protecting our own space. I guess I was afraid to lose what we had with each other. It seemed to give me something to hold onto. And so, I sat there engaging myself with my cigarette and watching the people in the coffee shop. What could be a better way to escape and deny what was happening in my own life than to focus outside of myself?

Occasionally, Dan would get up and walk to the phone booth just to make contact with the editorial office. Finally, he walked back to the table and said, "Let's go. I have to write an important news item." He extended his hand and we walked over to our little car. Competently, he wormed himself into the passenger's seat and reached over to open the door for me.

"Come on, my dear driver, and see that you drive carefully as I wish to arrive safe and sound." He glanced at his wristwatch. "I have only a half hour for the deadline so let's go."

Dan preferred not to drive. In fact, Dan had never gotten a driver's license. He claimed that driving a car was as risky and dangerous as using a machine gun. He believed that car accidents were very real possibilities and he wanted nothing to do with a potential fatality. "Cars are killing machines," he used to say. And so, for the most part, he used public transportation or he would hire a taxi. But, when we were together, I was the driver.

I inserted the key in the ignition and turned on the motor, but the only sound I heard was a weak and short whine followed by silence. "Try again," muttered Dan. I could see he was nervous now, pressured by time. He hated missing deadlines. Opening the window for air, he said, "Maybe it is not tuned properly."

"I don't know… Personally I think we got a lemon… This is not the first time… it was a mistake to buy it," I insisted knowing I was pouring oil on the blaze.

"Why are you telling me that? You always find a way to slap me in the face… I buy you a car and you spit in my face. I didn't ask you to thank me, but at least shut up about it." He got out of the car, slammed his door and opened the car hood, inspecting the motor and trying to test it out. "Try it now," he shouted. Again, there was nothing. Watching Dan through the windshield I could see how dirty the car was. I hadn't bothered to clean it in weeks. I felt quite uncaring about such things. Lately, I had crawled into myself and become totally indifferent. Sometimes it would frighten me… thinking of how I was turning into a sort of robot. Blindly, I obeyed the commands of the man in my life but inside I felt dead.

I wondered if our problems were different than other people's problems, if other couples had to face these challenges and difficulties, if they had to deal with anger and blame. I just wished that all the chaos would go away. I wished that the laughter and peace of our early relationship could magically return. But wishing was not enough to heal the past.

Right at that moment, I was awakened from my reverie by Dan's knock on my window, waving his hand for me to come out of the car. I rolled down the window. "It's getting late," he said. "Let's take a cab. This motor is dead. I'll send someone tomorrow to tow the car and fix it. I'll take care of it all," he added with a cynical smile on his face. I slowly emerged out of the car and closed the door behind me. He leaned forward, opened the door and slammed it so hard that the car shook. "Now it is closed," he said firmly.

Dan flagged down a taxi and impatiently waited for me to join him. He asked the driver to stop in front of our apartment building, opened the door for me, and sent me off with a quick kiss. "Go upstairs. I have to continue to the editorial office. I'll see you in a few hours."

I walked up the stairs with my head down. I don't know why exactly, but I was feeling shame. One more time I was accepting the blame for whatever had happened. I didn't know how it had been my fault but somehow I felt it was. I was torn between Dan's love for me and his restless, unpredictable behavior. Furthermore, I felt unable to reach back to my inner strength. Whatever had happened to my desire to live life to its fullest? Who could I really blame? It felt like I had abandoned myself. Reaching outside for approval and love, I had lost my very core, my essence.

Looking back at all those hours I had spent on the sand hill when I was a young girl, I realized how simple and innocent it had felt. How uncluttered and pure. I felt a strong desire to draw energy from there, to remember and to know that the possibility to be myself again was still rooted in me. No one could take that away from me unless I permitted it. Deep down inside I knew that I had let Dan take over. I had authorized him to be my owner, my creator. It was time for me to do something to gain myself back again.

When Dan returned home a few hours later, he carried in his hands a big bouquet of white orchids. He pushed the door open with his right shoulder and I heard him calling me. "My love, where are you?" As I crossed the room, he looked at me with a radiant smile on his face as if nothing had happened earlier.

"They are beautiful," I said, trying to take it all in. The uncertainty I had experienced only a few hours ago with Dan was forgotten and one more time I was on a merry-go-round.

All of a sudden, he appeared to be nearer and much more approachable to me. There was, one more time, a reason to keep standing by his side and try to repair our life together. He handed me the flowers and stretched himself out on the sofa. "One of these days I want us to have a child. I want our baby to be a boy… a real man… not a girl," he went on. "Girls are always chasing after their prey, and then they drive their teeth into its flesh." He drew away from me a little bit and looked at my face. "I am not talking about you. You are not an ordinary girl. I have molded you. I have shaped your personality the way it should be… Don't you agree?" He did not wait for an answer, but just kept on speaking. "When I first met you, you were neither a girl nor a boy," he laughed lightly. "I made you what you are now and it is absolutely mine."

I could feel the vague undercurrents of discontent rumbling in my gut but I just went on quietly. "I see," I said. "And, what will happen if we have a girl?"

"Here you go again. Why don't you just trust me? We will have a boy… trust me!" He fixed the pillow under his head and said with a second thought, "If we have a daughter, I will teach her to be like you: beautiful, naïve and obedient." He smiled as if he had found a solution.

"You think I am obedient?" I asked.

"You better be," he said laughing, and looking straight into my eyes.

"Well, sometimes it is because I have to be… not because I like it," I replied tentatively.

"What do you mean?" He raised his head and propped himself up on the pillow.

"I mean that sometimes I get fed up with being a parrot," I blurted out.

"Why?" He was surprised. "Have I ever disappointed you?" I noticed that his voice sounded worried.

"No, but sometimes I just like to be myself."

"Is that supposed to be a mini-revolution?!" he questioned seriously.

"Not a revolution at all. I wouldn't know how to revolt anyway," I responded, knowing inside that I was not completely telling the truth.

"Well, it doesn't matter why you are obedient as long as you are. That is the way I love you," he concluded. I looked at him and he smiled awkwardly. His two dimples ran along his cheeks deeper than ever before. "Come here. Get closer to me," and he pulled me lightly to his chest. "Sometimes I feel that nothing I do can make me feel better. But, when you are close to me, it is always better." He smiled and caressed my hair.

I nodded my head in agreement, appreciating his honesty. Moving even closer to him, I caressed his face, smoothing my hand over his forehead, his cheeks and his lips. He kissed me tenderly and pressed his face next to mine.

"Lately, I feel very old," he whispered.

"Old?" I giggled. "In January you will be only twenty-nine years old… that's not old."

"It is to me… You see," he explained slowly, "you don't count years with days and months. One should measure the years with life trials. Don't you think so?"

"This is way too philosophical… If it is so… I should be about a hundred years old now," I laughed.

"You are," he smiled. "You just don't know it."

"I don't think so," I insisted.

"You don't understand me." He did not wait for my answer and continued, "No one understands me, and when no one understands me… I consider myself nothing." He paused, then shook his head and moved to get up.

"Don't go." I held onto his body tightly. "It feels good just to be here together."

He relaxed his body and took a deep breath. "Okay," he said softly.

"So, where were we?" I asked trying to recapture the moment.

"It doesn't matter now…. Don't get me in trouble," he laughed.

"What do you mean? How could I possibly get you in trouble?"

"By telling you that I am nothing. You don't like it when I do that."

"I just don't get why you would think so. After all, people love you and respect you. How can you say you are

nothing? You have a great influence on people's opinions—why, almost every day you have a scoop and a headline in the paper."

"Yes, a headline in the paper. Big deal. Where do you
think all those newspapers end up? I've told you before—
in the toilet with people using them to wipe their ass!"

"Are you serious?" I asked. "Do you really think that's
all there is to it?" I felt sad for the two of us.

"Of course I'm serious. I'm very serious." He looked
me straight in the eye. "See, I told you that you don't
understand me." He kissed me on the cheek and smiled as
if to erase the last words from my mind. "But, it is okay. I
am not surprised you don't understand… I just have a different opinion about life… but don't worry about it. This
is too happy a moment to disagree."

"I just find it to be a sad opinion," I replied. "I wish you
could be happy for your achievements."

"Well, I am happy now," he said with a smile. "But, I
am entitled to my point of view." He drew his hand over
my face, examining every feature slowly. "I love you
madly," he said. "You are so naïve and so innocent. You are
everything I want." He passed his finger over my forehead
and let it slide down my nose. "You have a funny looking
nose you know, but I love it," and he squeezed me lightly.

Suddenly, I felt aloof and distant from this man who
was my husband. His words still rang in the air and his
affectionate comments about my nose and his love for me
did nothing to erase them. How could this man have such
a different opinion of himself than everyone else? It felt
disturbing and bizarre, and I couldn't get it out of my head
as we lay there together. I could feel the uncomfortable
space between us grow but nothing was said. I tried to

enjoy the warmth of our bodies and took pleasure in the beautiful possibilities that the future could hold.

As for Dan, he appeared to be in a reflective mood moving his right foot nervously back and forth.

"Are you okay?" I finally whispered.

"Of course I am okay. Why do you ask?"

I slanted my head to the right and pointed at his feet. He immediately stopped and began laughing. "You know, it is a habit of mine. My feet move on their own. I have no control over them," he said, laughing again. "Just as I have no control over you," he added playfully.

"Oh, of course you have control. At least over your feet," I added mischievously.

"I thought so. I should not fool myself about you," he smiled sadly. Then his face became somber. "You know, I was just laying here thinking. I would not like to die an old man needing support. I want to die straight and strong and handsome. I want to die at the peak of my career and be a man fit for remembering! Sick horses should be shot, you know. They aren't useful to anyone. They suffer and make others suffer." He sat up and straightened the pillows on the sofa. I had no immediate answer and Dan had not expected one. He got up and walked over toward the window.

After looking out at the city below for a few minutes, he pulled the curtains across and then walked back to me.

"You look pale... Did I shock you again?"

"Well, yes," I replied.

"Not to worry. Don't make a big deal out of everything... It's just my opinion and you don't have to agree with it."

Little did I know at the time that this conversation with Dan was more than just an easy afternoon talk. Little did I know that it was a serious reflection of one of his core beliefs about life and death.

Smiling again, he paused and said with renewed vigor, "Let's go have some dinner. I think I can eat now." Hand in hand, we walked out the door into the city below. Anyone looking at us would think we were a blissfully happy young couple.

CHAPTER 14

When the Words Became Alive

*Art is the language of the Soul. Its creative force has the power
to heal, alter lives and fulfill destinies.*
—Sara Shai

Since my marriage to Dan I had been made to feel somewhat worthy in my existence as a woman. I was treated with an extra sense of importance. I became a valuable member of my family and, in turn, of my society.

About four years after my wedding day, I received a call from my father. His voice was soft and somewhat hesitant. "This is your father," he said. A long pause followed. Was he waiting for me to acknowledge him? Was he concerned that I would not recognize his voice? True, the last time I had spoken with him was just before my wedding when I had invited him to take part in my celebration. But surely, he must know that I would recognize his voice. Finally, I said, "Father, I am so glad to hear from you."

"Congratulations!" he said. "It is never too late to congratulate you," he added with a nervous laugh.

"No, it is never too late," I agreed.

"I have always sent you good thoughts. I am happy for you... I heard that Dan is a good man... a respected man," he added.

"Thank you, Dad." I almost lost my voice—the tears felt like they were welling up inside of me. His caring and recognition for me after all these years was overwhelming.

"Sorry I didn't call earlier... Celina..." He seemed somewhat uncomfortable and I rushed to save him.

"I know," I said. "I understand, Dad." *It took her four years to allow him to speak to me,* I thought to myself. *What kind of a threat was I to her? What kind of fear did she have to protect herself from?*

"I am very happy for you," he repeated.

My response was immediate and filled with gladness. "Thank you, Dad. Thank you. Really, that means a lot to me." There was a heavy silence on the other end of the line—an uncomfortable feeling of intimacy played in the air. It was quite unfamiliar for both of us and hard to trust. But the desire to capture the sweet closeness I had once had with my father was as strong as ever. True, my experience with love's purity was somewhat short, but I still had it in me and I felt its innocence and wholesomeness. No special words were needed. I was thankful for the moment and I was grateful for what it was giving me.

"It is good. It is very good now. You are married to a good and respectful man. I heard all about him. He is a writer, a journalist. Ahh... I read sometimes his articles in the newspaper. I see his name." He was impressed and pleased to tell me. "I told your Grandma Lulu that I was going to call you and she sends her regards. In fact, she would like to pay you a visit." He waited for my reply.

"Of course. I would love to see Grandma Lulu, too."

"I will let her know," he replied and I could feel the pleasure in his smile. "Okay then. I will let her know and we will come to visit… It is good; it is very good. Give my regards to Dan. I will call you back," he concluded and rushed to hang up even before he could hear my next sentence.

"I will, Dad, and I am so glad you called…" There was already silence on the other end of the line. I put the receiver in its place and took a seat in a nearby chair. It was not a simple thing for my father to call and recognize me in spite of Celina's mocking. Moreover, his mother, my Grandma Lulu wanted to pay me a visit now. An acknowledgment and acceptance like I had never had before. A man had finally made an honest woman out of me and even though it had taken them years to accept it, I was now living and performing up to their expectations. The concern that I would go astray was finally removed. I knew that's what my father meant when he said, "It is good!"

And, indeed, it was good. It was so good that it even felt worthwhile to put up with Dan's controlling moods and tempers. After all, everything in life was a trade-off. This was my price to pay as long as I was able to swallow the bitter saliva quietly. For years now I had kept my face smiling and bright, not even aware most of the time of what I was doing and what was at stake. This approval was the reward I got for abandoning myself and leaving the sand hill behind. A high price indeed.

I told Dan that my father had called, while sitting with him at the café facing the Mediterranean Sea. I leaned toward him and kissed his face. "I feel so good. Can you believe it? My father called today," I continued with a childish excitement. "My Grandma Lulu would even like to pay us a visit. It is a big deal, you know. After all, I haven't seen my father since my visit to Ramleh the year after I graduated. I don't even remember when I saw my Grandma Lulu last." Dan listened quietly staring at my low-cut blouse. I leaned back in my chair contentedly.

"Why don't you wear that blouse tonight?" Dan said with no acknowledgement of our conversation.

"Their visit is a great honor," I said, but Dan remained silent. Watching me quietly, he finally said, "You are so very sexy… it is a pleasure to look at you… As for their visit… they should have given you this honor long ago…when we got married." He spoke straightforwardly, almost indifferently.

"It's okay. I know I am getting this honor because of you… they approve of me because of you."

"But why now?" he inquired still with some apathy.

"I suppose, at first they thought I got married to someone as ordinary as I am, or less. But when they found out that the man I married was someone as respected as you are… Well, then I became worthy of their acknowledgement." I said sincerely.

"It took them more than a few years to realize that!" He laughed. "This is a nice blouse," he murmured and drew me closer to him kissing my lips.

"Good news travels slowly," I agreed, avoiding his compliment and anxious to get back on the subject of my father.

"But how do you know it is because of me?" he asked with a hint of appreciation.

"I just know… and you know." I pointed at him gently. "I just know how they think. Trust me," I added.

"And why aren't you worthy in their eyes just on your own?" Dan knew the answer but needed to hear it one more time from me.

"You know the whole story with my mother," I said reluctantly, not sure I wanted to bring up the issue at all.

"Like mother, like daughter, eh?" He laughed while pulling his seat closer to me. "Well, time will tell." He looked at me with a smile that carried a great deal of weight.

"It is very hard to live life while being tested all the time." I pulled away from him. "It is an ugly burden." I looked straight into his eyes. Silently, I was demanding more from him. A word of assurance that in fact he was on my side. A sign of trust to put me at ease.

"Why are you looking at me like that?" he protested. "Anyway, it doesn't matter what I say or think," he came back at me.

"Yes, it does. Of course it matters what you say and think," I repeated after him for extra emphasis.

"Look… your own family doesn't respect you. Your father keeps on testing you. Why should I be any different?" he said.

"Because you, like me, had a mother who kept you in the shadow of shame. You, too, needed to protect the damn honor of your family. You, of all people, should know that!"

"Come on… I am just trying to show you that you can't please everyone. And it doesn't matter what they think," he corrected himself. "You think their visit is such a great deal. It is because you need their acceptance in order to prove your innocence. You need to be a 'good girl' for them. Well, it doesn't work that way."

"I didn't do anything wrong," I stated.

"That is precisely what I am trying to tell you!" He opened his hands in front of me.

"I don't care anymore," I mumbled. I was confused now.

"Listen to me. You are overlooking their insult. Not showing up at your wedding, not respecting you for who you are… just as long as they give you some of their backing in order for you to prove your innocence! Even when you know that their support is coming not because of who you are, but because of whom you married." He leaned back. "So the conclusion is that they still are not honoring you but only the one you married! Don't you see that?"

"Yes," I agreed quietly.

"So, my dear wife, you have got to understand that you cannot change people. It is impossible! It is your opinion that has to be altered and changed!" He looked at me for a long moment, examining me to see if I had grasped his input. I nodded softly. Then he raised his hand toward the waiter asking for the bill.

"It is the most difficult thing to do," he added, looking at my puzzled expression. "It means changing who you are!" he said while paying the bill. He took my hand and we left the café.

I knew Dan was right. Their opinion mattered so much to me and I seemed to settle for the crumbs. I was hungry and eager for emotional nourishment and I took anything handed to me with a grateful heart.

We took a stroll on the sidewalk next to the water, enjoying the clear night as many others did. On the beaches away from the streetlight, lovers were whispering and kissing. I glanced at them with an envious glow in my eyes as they stood protected in each other's arms. They represented a life full of meaning and joy—something beautiful that went beyond my vision.

And yet, even as young and inexperienced as I was, I somehow felt that my authenticity could not be completely violated or dishonored by anything or anyone, whether it be Dan or my family. It was whole and complete on its own. Even my own doing couldn't change it. In other words, my core authenticity became a witness to all that was happening and all that I was. It never judged me or abandoned me. It merely sat as a place of nurturing and safety, passionately waiting for an awakening. Although sometimes I felt as if I was sleepwalking, denying myself and just waiting for problems to go away, I somehow knew that no matter how hostile the world appeared to be, I would have that noble part in me as a place of empowerment and inspiration.

Lately, I had found comfort and fulfillment in my love of the creative arts. I had enrolled myself in a private art school in old Jafa in spite of Dan's objection. I recognized my passion for the creative process and continued to paint in oil and acrylic. I finally could communicate with the whole world without words, without worrying about agreement or disagreement. In art I could turn obscurity into bright light and with one stroke of the brush I could restore my natural and emotional pace. I also became involved with clay and experienced the wonderful sensation of bringing this medium to a complete birth. I carved in stone and was amazed to find life's expression in it.

Of course, the themes and images of my work emerged from the inner fabric of my life with its strengths and weaknesses. My engagement with the material was innocent, as I never planned the end result. Instead, I allowed the medium to develop its wish to be. It taught me the humility of becoming an instrument to see what was in it rather than what I wanted it to be. I found a place to be at total peace.

For me, to create was to feel alive, to live in the moment until it became real. Every creation was always a new and glorious rebirth. My passion for the creative arts seemed to have its own uncontrollable optimism. I could tune out all the ugliness and reclaim my innocence.

One day I sat down and wrote:

Art is the Language of the Soul
And as my soul speaks
In prayer, it whispers.
I silently listen.
The words become alive.
My hands move to create
At the rhythm of my heartbeat.
And while my lips are shut
I hear my inner voice.
Loud and clear… I can hear
I can watch
I can feel you in my fingertips,
Then I touch to create.
What a work of art.
And I know
In my heart, in my soul,
No doubt it is you;
God,
The woman in me,
The awaking woman of the now.

As I looked back over my words, I felt a surge of strength and love for myself. I knew I would triumph because my work came from a silent inner space within me. When I finished a piece of art, I felt as if I took part in God's work. It was the ultimate ecstasy, but would that be enough to guard me from the outburst ahead, or just a good escape?

CHAPTER 15

The Headline

Do not weep, do not wax indignant. Understand.
—Baruch Spinoza (1632-1670)

In the following year we moved to a new and larger apartment in the prestigious section of northern Tel Aviv. It was two blocks away from the Mediterranean shore, on the top floor overlooking the entire city. We were the envy of many of our young friends and my family was thrilled with Dan's success. Everything appeared to be going well except that it was becoming even harder for me to be at the mercy of Dan's unpredictable moods and his temper. Dan was promoted to a higher position at the newspaper and his work took on a stronger intensity with equivalent demands.

It was early fall, late at night, when Dan went down to the print room in his editorial office. He looked into the paper that was printed for the next day, folded one of them and pushed it under his left arm.

"It's too late. I will take a look at it at home," he said to the night editor. When he arrived home, it was already after 11:00 p.m. He kissed me lightly and sat in his favorite armchair. He had an intense look on his face and appeared to be thinner than usual. Looking at him I knew it was better for me to stay out of the way. His long thin fingers turned the pages feverishly while his eyes searched intently from under his smooth hair that covered his entire forehead. He was nervously moving his feet from side to side, back and forth, obviously troubled.

"How are you?" he asked with his face still buried in the paper.

"I'm fine," I said.

"Good, come sit next to me… I just need to finish reading this." I joined him, following his reactions until he looked at the headline of the political section. At last… there was his reward… a byline over his news item. Dan opened his eyes wide, put his hand on his forehead and pulled his hair back. He looked close at the printed words with disbelief and shouted with full savage fury. "I knew it… I knew it! He buried my news item. That son of a bitch night editor. He hates me, I tell you… He hated it when I put my scoop on his desk. He just buried it… he might as well have thrown it into the basket!"

Dan threw the paper on the floor and stalked to the telephone with rage. He sat at the kitchen table and dialed the editor-in-chief's number. Picking the newspaper up off the floor, he placed it on his lap. "Let me talk to him," Dan rasped at the secretary. She switched the line quickly and Dan lowered his tone of voice. "Sir, the news item I talked to you about a few hours ago should be a headline. Tomorrow, all the afternoon papers will copy it. It's a true scoop. I got the information directly from the Army Chief of Staff. It was a private talk… and he gave me the go ahead to print it… I had it approved by the censor, which was not an easy thing to do." Dan made an effort to keep his cool but I could see it was not easy. "It is buried at the bottom of the page… might as well not print it at all!"

There was a short silence.

"I have the first layout for tomorrow's paper in my hands." He tapped on the paper in his hand and listened to the voice at the other end. Finally, he said, "True, it is not the final print yet." There was relief in his voice. "Good. You will see to it personally, is that what you're saying?" Dan repeated the editor's words to make certain they understood each other. "Yes, yes. I'll take it easy… but first it has to be right… yes. Well, good night to you, too, sir." He placed the receiver in its place slowly and smiled to himself with satisfaction.

"We shall see," he said and stretched his legs on top of the coffee table. "So he will personally go down to the print room and see that it will get the best exposure." Dan repeated the editor's promise to me, but immediately he added, "We shall see tomorrow morning… we shall see. You can't trust anyone anymore."

He took his jacket off. "Can I have something to drink… maybe something to eat, too?" I was on my way to the kitchen when he changed his mind. "Actually, just hot cocoa will do." He seemed pleased with himself. A few minutes later I placed the tray on the table and sat on the sofa across from him.

"That was good," I said carefully.

"Not good enough. I am becoming a robot." He nodded his head and spoke calmly but his voice was full of intensity. "A robot that reports any move on the part of the Arab world and its leaders. How do you like that? You're married to a robot. If some Kurd in the north of Iraq makes up his mind to sneeze… why I just report it on my damned typewriter. It's enough that Nasser might raise his hand over his head and that sends me typing furiously. Should five consumptive Yemenites, doomed to death anyhow, find a much easier death from the bombardment of their Egyptian friends, they will move me again to run to my typewriter." He reached for his hot cocoa, held the cup in both hands and took a long sip.

"So, that's what I am… just a robot. A typing robot." He paused and I watched his face change and become grim and pale. "Sometimes I have a headache from the mere sound of my typing. So what do you think now that you know who I am. You are married to a robot." He laughed an artificial laugh and dropped his arms to his sides. I remained quiet, not exactly sure what to say. "So, what do you think now?" he asked and pushed me lightly with his feet as if to awaken me.

"I think you are the cutest robot I have ever been married to."

"Good girl. I think so, too. Cute, huh? So you think I am cute… and you don't care that I am a robot?" He laughed again.

"I only care about the way you view yourself. No robot can do what you are doing."

"Don't make me laugh," he said finishing his drink and placing the empty cup on the tray. "I did not expect you to understand. I am tired from all the bullshit in this world. People killing people. The Middle East will never become a peaceful place. It is a hopeless place. You will see. They simply don't want us here. And we don't have anywhere else to go." He laughed a bitter laugh. "Sometimes I feel like the Jewish nation. No one wants me and I don't have anywhere to go."

"Why are you saying that? I…"

"Yes. Yes," he cut me off. "That's what you're saying now. Wait and see… I'll bet you won't want to be with me forever," he challenged me. "It is not easy to be with me. Look, even my own mother left me. I don't want you to turn out to be like my mother or your mother for that matter… life is not easy… life is not as important as people make it to be."

"What do you mean, 'life is not important?'" I wondered out loud.

"Let's go to sleep. Tomorrow is another day." He ignored my question and got up, taking my hand and pulling me gently after him to the bedroom. "I am tired," he said after putting on his pajamas and stretching his body next to mine. He hugged me and I felt numb. He kissed me lightly and I froze in my place. When he moved to his side of the bed and said, "Good night," I was relieved.

I could not sleep, however. I rolled on my side and kept looking for rest. Dan's last remark had hit me hard. Like a deadly blow, I could not find the remedy. I could not find clarification for what he had said. I hated Dan right then. I hated him for fearing that I would become like his mother or mine. I hated him for labeling me and treating me as a wrongdoer, especially now when I was thinking that I had successfully put my family at ease. Here I got it back in my face from my own husband, in my own home. Was this some kind of conspiracy from a Higher Source or was it just a coincidence? To have married a man with such a bad experience with his own mother.

I curled my body and turned over again. "Go to sleep,"

I heard Dan whispering.

"I can't sleep."

"Count sheep. Up to one hundred the way I do it. You will see it will help. It always works for me."

Apparently, it did help, as it was nearly six o'clock when Dan entered the bedroom with the morning newspaper. He sat on the edge of the bed and scanned the first page. "It is a headline all right. Just the way it should be!"

"I am not surprised," I said still somewhat sleepy.

"Yes… but I still hate that night editor. He will hear from me today."

"But, you got your way."

"What do you mean? It could happen again… The son of a bitch hates my guts!"

"Maybe it's just in your mind," I said getting up from the bed and putting on my robe.

"Just in my mind?" He was angry.

"I am sorry," I said immediately. "I didn't mean it in a bad way… I just can't imagine why he would hate you."

"Because," he laughed. "People hate me!" he concluded assertively.

"It is not good to think like this," I said on my way out of the bedroom.

"Wait a minute. You are still telling me what to think and what to say? Don't you understand how absurd that is… to actually tell me what to think." Dan was clearly annoyed with me, and he did not stop there. "Are you a stubborn woman or just plain stupid?" His voice didn't change and his question was sort of matter-of-fact, simply wondering about me aloud.

I was aggravated but did not say much. I walked out of the bedroom and Dan followed me. "That's all right," I

heard him saying behind me. "I don't think you hate me...
do you?"

"No." I turned toward him, but was upset and still too
apprehensive about Dan's state of mind. I pictured him to
be like the poet who always tears himself to pieces just
because his sonnet is not equal to that of Shakespeare's.

He shrugged his shoulders and went back into the bedroom. A few minutes later I heard the shower running. I
remained standing in the middle of the living room thinking about our life together. We were the envy of many people and appeared to have everything one could want. We
had all the ingredients for a good life, but here behind
closed doors there was nothing to envy or desire. Each and
every moment was unpredictable. Every time we seemed to
find a moment of joy, right away it was pulled down and
taken away. It felt like a slap in the face. The unquiet mind
of Dan was desperately searching for peace and calm, and
yet he seemed to deliberately cut off the flow of every possibility for intimate connection and peace to flower. I
could not help but feel frustrated and angry with myself for
not having the courage to take a stand for myself.

When Dan got out of the shower wrapped in a towel,
I noticed him glancing at me with strange look of concern.
"Are you all right?"

"Not sure," I said thoughtfully.

"Why 'not sure'? What's the matter with you... why do
you look so miserable? You hate me, don't you?" He took
a few steps toward me.

"No, I don't. I don't hate you." I moved away not lik-
ing the look in Dan's eyes. Rage and an unexplainable
force.

"How can you hate me? I do so much for you. Look

around you. Everything you have here comes from me... Look at yourself; I made you. You came from the gutter of Ramleh and I made you what you are."

I remained frozen in my place wishing for him to stop. There was a short silence, a deadly hush. A painful sensation took over, but I knew that Dan was not finished yet. "Really, who do you think you are anyway? Who would take you in? Your stepmother or your stepfather? The truth is you need me more than you are willing to admit. No one has ever wanted you. So you need to learn one thing..." He raised his hand up and said, "Don't ever tell me what to do or what to think." He walked toward me slowly, grabbed my head with both hands and brought my face close to his. "Don't tell me what to do." He released my head from his grip and quickly raised his hand and slapped my face.

I was stunned. Shocked. I held my cheeks with both hands and cried silently. He, too, was stunned, not believing his own action. Instantly, he was sorry. "I am sorry... really sorry... I didn't mean to hurt you." He moved away wishing to bring the past back. He reached for me wanting to hold my hand but I moved away. He looked at me with distress and dropped his arms helplessly.

What had just happened was something out of a different realm. It was a moment of insanity. I had seen Dan's face change and become full of rage and out of control. This was the first time Dan had used force. It did not take too long for him to come back and get hold of himself. It was as if he was crossing back over from a different world. Dan walked restlessly around the living room searching for an answer. I tried my utmost to calm down but a sharp feeling penetrated through me. A heavy trembling shook my whole body. I realized I had been marching with Dan all that time in the dark. There was no turning back and all of a sudden there was nothing to bind us together. I walked out to the porch and looked out into the empty space.

"I need to go... I'm going to be late for work," I heard him saying. He went into the bedroom for a few moments and then walked back into the living room adjusting his tie. "I said I have to go now," he called to me. I ignored his wish, as I knew he wanted me to escort him to the front door as I always did.

I heard the front door open and immediately slam shut. I knew Dan had left. I looked back down at the street below and saw him walking slowly, contrary to his usual habit. He raised his head and looked to see me. Lowering his head, he kept on walking as if to count the number of tiles on the pavement. He stopped, bent down and picked up an old newspaper. After he looked at it, he folded it and carefully, almost with respect, put it at the edge of the sidewalk. I kept on watching him walking away until I lost sight of him.

Alone, I remained vulnerable and drained. I had no fast answer and could not fathom the meaning behind Dan's behavior. I blamed him for failure; I blamed him for breaking down.

That night, Dan came home earlier than usual, carrying a large slice of chocolate cake with whipped cream. His hands were sticky with the sweet repast. He walked into the kitchen and halved it with a big carving knife. "You know," he said to me while licking his fingers with joy. "You know, I was walking on the street among the crowd feeling completely lonely." He waited for me to say something, but I kept quiet. "This is not good… I think maybe something is wrong with me," he continued speaking unemotionally while offering me a piece of cake on the tip of the fork.

"Take some; it is good... a little sweet is always good for the soul." He handed me the fork, which I took from him and made an effort to smile.

"I am sorry you felt lonely," I said.

"Just forget that. The cake, the sweet cake, is it good?" He consumed the cake with pleasure as if he had found an exalted and lofty solution, speaking about loneliness on the crowded street of Tel Aviv, and reaching for a divine sweetness that could be purchased with a chocolate cake and whipped cream. We ate the cake standing up. I noticed that some of the white whipped cream was sticking to his mustache and I reached out and wiped the cream away.

"You care?" he asked softly.

"I am not sure anymore." I shrugged my shoulders coldly.

"I see... I really hurt you this morning."

"I think we should talk," I said sincerely.

"Okay... what is on your mind?" he asked with some concern. I gathered strength and walked toward the sofa and sat down.

"What is it that you want to talk about?" He walked toward me while loosening his tie. "Do I need to sit down also?"

"I think so," I replied.

"You sound dead serious." He was concerned.

"I think we should see a psychologist," I said quickly, and added, "It would be good for us." I felt very sure of my suggestion.

"You must be joking. You want to send me to a shrink?" he laughed loudly. "You really think I am crazy, a madman?" He was bewildered.

"Not a madman," I said quietly. "It would be good for us, you and me."

"I am not so stupid! You say you and me just to get me there. I am not the crazy one here." He watched me with disbelief. "See, I shouldn't have told you that I felt lonely. I shouldn't confide in you! I am not crazy, not a madman." He was disappointed and moved his feet back and forth in a nervous motion as he usually would when in anxious moments. I wasn't entirely surprised by Dan's reaction. I was aware of how a visit to the psychologist could affect his reputation. I knew of the stigma of needing mental help and I understood how this would affect Dan's image of himself. No matter how confidential we would keep it, still Dan could not bear the fact that he needed to seek mental help.

"It is out of the question... just forget about it!" He stood up and faced me directly. "I'll tell you what," he said and touched my hand with the pretense of a friendly gesture. "I'll tell you what. Why don't you go to the psychologist and let me know about his diagnosis?" He couldn't help laughing. "That would be a good headline. I promise to get it in the paper on the front page."

I remained sitting. Looking at him from my angle, he seemed bigger and stronger, defiantly confident in his position.

Sometimes life or death hangs in the balance of a single decision. I've always wondered if deciding against seeing the psychologist had cost Dan his life.

CHAPTER 16

A Stormy Time

It is not true that life is one damn thing after another. It is one
damn thing over and over.
—Edna St. Vincent Millay

The following month, November 1970, was an unsettling and stormy time in our relationship. Each and every
encounter we had made us appear smaller in each other's
eyes. But we continued blaming each other out of a mixture of anger and insecurity. We weren't ready to give up on
our marriage. If anything, we wanted to keep on trying for
the sake of our families and tradition, but the old beliefs of
our culture and the stereotyping of men and women had
come crashing down upon us, and I didn't know how to
emerge out of its ruins.

This tear between Dan and myself was a painful one. I
annoyed him and he would go into a tirade of physical and
verbal rage. Nights dragged slowly and they became a sour
threat for me. Sometimes, during those nights and the days
that followed, I accepted the fact that Dan and I were not

meant to be together any longer. I felt a loss and anguished over our failure. I desperately needed the compassion of someone loving and caring. One day, I thought of sharing my pain with my Aunt Doris and so I confided in her about my troubles with Dan's demands and control.

"I don't think it is so bad," she responded afterward. "He loves you, we all know that, and so what if he wants his way? He is the man. For God's sake, he should have his way!"

"Yes, but you don't understand. He is very hurtful."

"How? How is he hurtful?" she challenged me.

"By telling me to go back to the boarding school, that no one would want me anyway."

I waited for her acknowledgement and was disappointed when she countered with, "So what, he simply was angry. People say all kinds of things when they are angry."

I got very quiet.

"What is so bad?" she finally asked. "Maybe you are not telling me everything."

"I fear the nights, " I reluctantly charged, wishing for her compassion.

"Why?"

"I can't make love to him… He will hurt me like that and then he will want to make love to me right after… I can't… I don't know what to do… it's awful," I mumbled holding back my tears.

"I see," she said and smiled with a sense of sympathy. "Now I understand." She put her arm around my shoulder and took a deep breath. "Come here, sit next to me," and she began sharing her woman's wisdom with me.

"A woman needs to be receptive and giving of her body to her husband regardless of how she feels or what she wants." She spoke slowly as she had a good inclination that

I would reject her opinion. "Listen, what is the big deal? You just let him do what he needs to do, ahh?" she asked simply.

"What are you saying, Aunt Doris?" I looked at her with surprise. "I can't do that!" Shaking my head in disagreement, I took a second glance at her and saw she was still smiling. I slowly asked, "Can you do that?"

"Of course… all the time… Why are you so surprised?" She seemed to find me so immature.

"Well, I don't think I can… I can't open my body to him when he is so mean to me." I lowered my head but kept on speaking with a clear and solid voice. "In fact, I don't know how it is possible at all," I raised my head and looked at her questioningly again.

"It is possible all right," she laughed lightly. "This is the way of life. Do you think I enjoy sex the way my husband enjoys it. No, no, no… I just put up with it. It is only a few moments and it is done."

I could not help but remember my girlfriend, Shoshana, describing her first intercourse with her newlywed husband.

"This is the price a woman must pay," my aunt concluded.

"Pay for what?" I was enraged.

"For everything your husband does for you… it is an unspoken fact, you silly girl." She got up and spread her arms as if she had no more to say. I remained sitting, looking at her with a mixture of confusion and disbelief.

"Well, this is not what I think love is," I exploded.

"Love, love, love, what is it anyway? Everyone is talking about love these days." She sat down next to me again as if the tables were turned and she was wishing to draw some wisdom from me.

"Maybe it is respecting each other, respecting each other's feelings. Maybe that's what love is all about. Respect! I don't know... but certainly it cannot be what you are describing," I insisted.

"Respect? Of course, my husband respects me. Why else would he marry me in the first place?" She paused and added pointing at herself, "And I, in return, respect his needs," she said with winning conviction.

"How about your feelings and wishes. You don't count?!"

"You are too poetic, too romantic. Wake up silly girl... this is real life not a fairy tale."

"So, you think I am asking too much?" I inquired.

"Yes." She seemed happy to agree with me. "Yes, and listen here. You go back to Dan. He is a wonderful man... you are lucky to have him... don't put any of that love crap in your head... it did not help your mother did it?"

It is worth noting that after this conversation with my Aunt Doris I did not share my pain with anyone, and did not feel the need to consider someone else's insight. I now knew what the reaction would probably be, and I did not believe I would get any positive support from anyone. In the real world, where I lived, there was no place for romanticism and idealism. It was only in my vision and my desire to achieve it. I believed I had no solid argument against Dan and I did not want to take my dirty laundry out into the open. I supposed it was my personal and unique pain and so I felt that I wanted to address it my own way. My marriage seemed to have failed and I wanted out. A divorce seemed like the only answer.

That evening I joined Dan in our living room. He was reading the evening paper and listening to the Arabic radio station.

"Dan, I want to talk to you," I said.

"What now?" he asked while still reading.

I paused first, and then said in one long breath, "I want a divorce."

He raised his head, dropping the paper on the coffee table and looked at me sharply. "A divorce? Over my dead body... I will never give you a divorce," and he grabbed his paper again and returned to reading, angrily dismissing the issue.

"Dan, I mean it. Don't ignore this one."

"Look here," he raised his voice and pointed his finger at me. "I knew this was coming and I am telling you NO! I am not ignoring this one at all... I would rather die before giving you a divorce. Do you understand me?" He picked up the newspaper from the coffee table, fixed the pages and held the paper in front of his face. Although he was no longer looking at me, he continued talking. "I am not giving you a divorce. Shame on you for asking such a thing. Just because your parents are divorced you think it is an acceptable move. No. No, not in my home. I am not giving you a Gett," he concluded. Once more he reiterated, "I am not giving you a Gett."

Although Judaism accepted divorce as a fact of life, the position of a husband and wife regarding a divorce was not an equal one. For years, under Jewish law, a husband as the head of his family could divorce his wife at will for any reason, or for no reason at all. The wife, on the other hand, could not enforce a divorce regardless of the reason. Only later on, did rabbinical authorities take steps to ease the severity of those rules by prohibiting a man from divorcing a woman without her consent. Still, the rabbinical court's position was to do everything possible to prevent the tear of the holy marriage document, the Ketuba. The document of divorce was referred to in the Talmud as a *Sefer K'ritut* (the scroll of cutting off) but it is commonly known today as a *Gett*. Dan was letting me know he would not give his approval for the *Gett* without which I would have a great deal of difficulty acquiring the divorce.

For the remainder of the night, Dan was quiet and very thoughtful. He and I had taken contrary positions and not for a moment had we moved toward an understanding. We were each like ships that were torn away from our anchor.

As days passed, his withdrawn anger turned into depression and he was more and more restless at night. "I wish I could sleep," he said. "Sleep is quiet and soothing. It's as sweet as death must be," he told me one night.

It seemed that his world had become unbearable. He was skipping meals and isolating himself from the outside world. Every time I offered some clarification he pushed me away. He stayed in bed for long periods of time and told me that he was tired and wished to be left alone. "I don't want to see anyone!"

One day he shared his feelings with me. "I feel trapped in a dark void," he said. "Sometimes I'd like to leave that endless hole but, for the most part, it feels safe and I'd like to be taken away by it. I just want to turn away and go to sleep... slip into that sweet, peaceful sleep and not come back. I am not sure which is better... madness or death. I simply want the world to leave me alone."

I sat on the edge of the bed, my body feeling heavy and frozen, and I couldn't utter a word. Noticing my worried response, and my earlier wish to call a therapist, ended his reverie quickly. "Look, I'm sorry I worried you. It is not really as bad as it sounds. I just need rest for a few days. I made a call to my editor and told him not to bother me unless it was urgent… I need the rest that's all… Just give me some time… I will snap out of this dark hole, I promise," he laughed and asked me to leave the room.

I was infuriated now and raised my voice. "I don't believe you… you are always talking about death!"

"And why can't I talk about death? What is wrong with it, I want to know? What is it about death that no one wants to hear? What is the fear?" He spoke clearly with conviction. "People are afraid of death because they don't know enough about it… the mystery scares them," he stated. Then he faced me directly. "Tell me something. Are you afraid of death?"

"I don't know… I don't think about it," I replied. I looked back at him, listening closely as he spoke in a sincere yet detached mode.

"Maybe you should think about death… after all, it is something that we all have to encounter sooner or later… Maybe, just maybe, it is not such a bad thing. Think about it… Look at that clock," and he pointed to the clock on our kitchen wall. "Listen to the ticking… it is only a friendly reminder that death is near… so what is wrong about getting to know it?"

"I don't know, Dan… We have many years to live and I prefer to make them pleasant and happy that's all." My anger was gone and I lost interest in the discussion.

" Are you afraid?" he inquired eagerly.

"No."

"Are you afraid of me?" he asked again.

"No."

"Good, because I will never harm you. I love you."

"I know," I whispered.

He smiled with kindness. "It is too much to handle for you," he explained.

"It's late. I am tired," I said quietly, wishing to close the subject.

"I am too stressed and too tired to sleep," he said. "And don't think about bringing up the idea of a therapist again… I am not one of your damn students," he snapped.

It was as if he had read my mind. I had so many mixed emotions and sometimes a sense of fear for Dan and myself. I was very careful about what to say and how to say it. I understood that it was important for me to assert myself but I had to be loving at the same time. His constant speaking about death unnerved me. True, it was too much for me to handle, and I wished to seek help now more than ever, but I knew Dan would never allow it. It was out of the question.

His restlessness continued. Every little thing would trigger an argument. Often he would go into the editorial office for a few hours and then rush back home, managing his writing from the living room and getting in heavy quarrels and disagreements with the editor-in-chief over the phone.

"I will be going to the occupied territories for this investigation," I heard Dan say to his friend one night on the phone.

"You've never had to go to the front line before," I commented when he hung up from his conversation.

"Well, I'm going now!" he said. "I will be going to the Lebanon border with our troops. We're leaving tomorrow morning, just for one day… I got a license for a gun and I purchased one… a good one," he said with a strange little smile on his face. I tried not to think too much but Dan was able to sense my concern. "Don't be afraid, " he said after a short silence. "I am not afraid at all."

When Dan returned form his trip he said, "I missed you... I could not think of anything but you, so you better take the thought of that divorce out of your pretty little head completely."

I never mentioned it again, but deep down Dan knew that I had been frank and sincere in my request.

"I know that I've hurt you so many times," he told me one evening after a deep and gloomy silence, "but I'd like to have another chance." He was struggling with his words and brushed his hair away from his forehead with his fingers. "Look... I promise to change. Please, don't leave me." He did not even try to hide his tears. "I feel so lonely... so sorry... don't leave me, please don't leave me." He was pleading and I was dumbfounded.

"I won't. I won't," I said quickly.

A fierce sob of relief and grief shook his body. He slowly slid and rested himself on the sofa, covered his face with both hands and cried as a little child would. I moved closer to him and wrapped my arms around him. His body was shivering; his forehead was covered with perspiration and his knees moved rapidly in a back and forth motion. I could smell the strong odor of his perspiration. Feeling helpless, I leaned my head on his shoulder. He kept on crying and I kept on holding him. I was wrong about men being tough and not sensitive. I was wrong about men being the superior ones. I felt wrong about so many things as I sat there holding him, feeling humbled in his presence.

We both sat there for a long time immobilized with pain till Dan's cries became softer and somewhat calmer. I was listening to his heavy breathing while I reminisced back to our first meeting, our hopes and promised life together. I wondered about us being the envy of so many people, while now we seemed to be the most vulnerable and helpless ones on the face of the earth.

"If you leave me, I will kill myself," he whispered. Freeing himself from my arms, he faced me. "I mean it. If you leave me, I will kill myself." He waited for me to say something but I was speechless. "Besides, it is better for you to be my widow than to be my divorcee...you understand that... don't you?"

I remained silent, not knowing how to take it all in.

"So... do I have your promise... there will be no divorce? Not a divorce, not in my home. End of subject!" He waited for my reply and I finally spoke.

"End of subject. No divorce," I repeated after him.

"That's good," he smiled. Kissing me, he got up with renewed energy and as if we'd played with magic, the dark depression lifted. "You won't be sorry... I will make it up to you," and he seemed content.

From this point on, Dan seemed to take things more lightly and he was especially agreeable and thoughtful. One day in early December, he returned home from the editorial office carrying many gifts and a wide smile on his face. He placed everything on the table and called me over.

"Remember when I promised you a second honeymoon?" he whispered and kissed my cheek.

"Yes, I remember."

"So, we are going tomorrow. We are leaving to Eilat tomorrow, early morning." He slid his hand into his jacket pocket and handed me the flight tickets. Taking my hand, he lovingly walked with me toward the sofa. He leaned forward and kissed me on my lips with passion. "You always taste so good." He kissed me again holding my head tightly with both hands. Slowly, his hands slid down to my shoulders and he began to unbutton my blouse. I moved away quickly, releasing myself from his grip and with no struggle at all he let me go.

"You hate me, don't you?" he asked bitterly. "I repulse you."

"I don't hate you," I said, fixing my blouse but inwardly feeling confused at my own feelings.

"Don't lie," he said irritated, but quickly seemed to dismiss his feelings and attempted to put the tension to rest. "Anyway, listen... I always keep my promises. So we are going to have a second honeymoon to celebrate our new life together." Dan examined my face intently while I was buttoning up my blouse.

"We are leaving early tomorrow morning." He placed the tickets on the table.

"I had better start packing now, then," I said, and got up to move.

"Don't go." He got up and walked toward the window. "Stay here with me. Look out this window. You see so many people, so many lives... Everyone thinks he is the one that matters... Every one is a God of his own creation... Everyone is right."

"True," I replied. "Everyone is a whole world."

I don't think he heard me as he now was leaning on the edge of the window with his chin pressed into his locked hands in deep thought. "Did you say something?" He lifted his head and casually looked at me. Suddenly, he picked me up and heaved me over his shoulder. I could not help but laugh upside down all the way to the bedroom. He dropped me down on the bed and laughed himself.

"I am getting old... picking you up was a hard thing to do." He looked down at me.

"I am getting fat," I laughed.

"No, I am getting old."

"Oh yes… your birthday is coming up. I forgot." I held on to his leg and got up laughing.

"Ahh, my birthday… what a sweet time that shall be," and he threw me back on the bed. "And really who cares about my birthday? Who cares about me?" he said becoming somewhat serious.

"I do." I pulled him next to me. We both lay on our backs looking up at the ceiling. "You can't improve the whole world at once. All you can do is improve your own life."

"You think so?" he smiled thoughtfully.

"Yes," I said humorously.

"You're smart. Just like a teacher should be. So you think I have to improve myself, eh?" he inquired. "I don't think so my dear lady. I can't improve on myself… I am already nothing." He stood up and leaned against the door-frame looking at me with some disappointment. "We always come back to the same damn point… You want to change me and I want to be me… how sad… You want me to be happy and I am happy to be me, sad or not."

"I did not mean to upset you now," I said.

"I know. It is not you. It's me… really, it's me," he said softly. You still don't know me. Maybe in time." His gaze was deeply penetrating. A silence fell between us, a very deep silence, and I wished to stay in this quiet place.

As I close my eyes now, I can still remember the warm room, the dark golden wood armoire, the tall mirror with its carved wooden frame, the king size soft bed, the high ceiling above it, and the layers of beautiful sheer curtains peeking out from under the draping fabric of taffeta all bounced and gathered on the floor. On the chair in the far corner I had stacked a few of my favorite hats and scarves that Dan had bought for me on his various trips. I could hear the raindrops hit lightly on the glass windowpanes and the sound of the easy wind playing in the background. Amid the jumble of feelings, a trip to the desert resort city of Eilat sounded just right.

The next day we took the morning flight to Eilat. Dan had a reservation at the same hotel where we had begun our honeymoon, six years ago. The desert met the Red Sea exactly the way we had left it. Dan had wanted to have the same room but it was already occupied. That evening we went down to the café by the sea. Multicolored lights reflected in the calm water. The moon hung above us in all its fabulous beauty. Soft music played all around and the easy warm desert wind caressed our bodies. I was wearing a soft sleeveless white dress and tied my hair with a chiffon scarf. Everything was beautiful and I felt very content and relaxed. Dan pulled up two chairs for us and placed them on the sand as close as possible to the water. The waves hit lightly and broke beneath our feet. I took my sandals off and stuck my feet in the water. It was an enchanting night, the kind of night that God created for lovers and carefree people.

The café was crowded and many people seemed to be enjoying the wonder of the surroundings. A waiter approached us and Dan ordered a bottle of red wine and an appetizer. "It is beautiful here," I said.

"You are beautiful," he smiled and poured the wine.

"Thank you, Dan," I laughed.

"That white dress against your dark skin. It is magnificent... white should be your color... pure and clean." He picked up his glass of wine and looked around the café, his eyes following the people. "Too many old people," he remarked.

"I wonder how I will look in my old age?" I asked, and took my first sip from my wine.

"I, for one, don't have any such worries," Dan retorted. He was absorbed in a group of old men and women gathered at the next table. An old woman was pulling forward a chair for her companion who supported himself on a walking stick.

"Look, what do I need that for?"

"He seems to be happy," I said, pointing at the old man tapping his foot to the tone of the music in the background. "Look at him, he is enjoying the music."

"Not for me... not for me at all."

It was after midnight when we reached our suite. Feeling good and loved, I threw my scarf on the bed and said, "I am going to take a bath." I walked into the bathroom and turned on the water.

"In that case, shut the door. The noise disturbs me," Dan said. He threw his body on the bed, stretched out in an oblique position and rearranged the pillow under his head, hugging the second one close to his body. His gaze was fixed on the ceiling.

The touch of the water filled me with gaiety. I still was enjoying this enchanted night, this second honeymoon, this new beginning. I wanted to allow trust to grow within me again. I smiled full of loving energy and sensuality. I sank farther into the bath and pushed the door open with my foot. "Hello there," I called to Dan in a dreamy voice.

"Will you join me?"

Dan raised himself up slowly and walked over to the bathroom door. He leaned on the doorjamb and examined me. His eyes were wide open as I splashed around in the bath water. He had a certain smile and look on his face. It was the first time I had ever noticed Dan looking at me like that. It was a look that seemed to know something considerably important. It was a mysterious look that seemed loaded with information, a look that followed me for many, many years later without clarification. It was only in looking back that I could recall that look, that gaze, the appearance of those big dark eyes being fixed and almost numb. I remember his eyes as if they were hanging all over me for a long time and I could not release myself from their insistent request and demand. Dan stayed leaning on that doorjamb for a long time… so long that I felt uncomfortable in my nakedness and wished to cover myself, wished I could pull the clear water together and hide beneath it. Then he moved slightly back, passed a frozen, vacant stare all along my body, caught hold of the door handle and vehemently closed the bathroom door.

A few minutes later I wrapped myself with a big towel and approached Dan. "What happened?" I asked.

"Nothing happened … you should stop your silly performance."

"What do you mean?"

"Nothing… I don't really feel comfortable talking about it."

"What is it? I need to feel part of you… I need you to tell me how you feel… now that we want to have a new beginning. You said a second honeymoon, a new beginning." I looked at him.

"You really want to be a part of me?" he asked with a doubtful voice.

"Yes."

"But it is not good to be part of me." His voice shook with emotion and he waved his hands strongly. "You see, I stood up and was watching you in the tub... I was feeling ashamed of you... something came over me." He held his head with both hands and continued. "I felt ashamed of your nakedness... I could not see you naked. That frightened me!" Our eyes met as he looked up and a heavy silence fell between us. "Are you surprised?" he asked quietly.

"I don't know... do you suppose something is wrong with me?" I ventured after a pause in which I tried to overcome my astonishment. How easily I fell into the role of the guilty one.

"Oh no, not at all. You are beautiful. You are very beautiful. My God look at your body. Your body is beautiful. Your dark hair..." and he touched my hair lightly and forced a smile. "It is me, it is me... I don't care for..." he stopped short. "I mean I really love you, you know, but so help me God, I can't pretend any longer," he whispered, touching his forehead with trembling fingers and brushing his hair back with his palms. "Yes, there is definitely something wrong with me." he murmured low.

I looked at him, wishing to say something kind, but my voice would not obey my will and the words would not come out. "It is okay," I finally said.

"What's okay? What do you know?"

"I mean it is okay no matter what," I lied.

I clearly lied. Because deep in my heart I wished to ask *why was he ashamed of my body? Why was he afraid, and what did he mean when he said, I can't pretend any longer?*

CHAPTER 17

The Ballet

*A little sincerity is a dangerous thing, and a great deal of it is
absolutely fatal!*
—Oscar Wilde

We left Eilat on the morning of December fourth, flying across country to the busy city of Tel Aviv. As we exited the airport holding hands and engaged in a relaxed conversation, I noticed that the sun was shining and especially bright for this time of the year. It was a perfect temperature but I was glad to have my light sweater over my shoulders. Dan called for a taxi and informed the driver to drop me off at our apartment and then continue on to his editorial office.

"I need to work for a change," he laughed as the driver pulled up to our apartment. "I will be home early tonight. Maybe we should eat out and see a movie." He blew me a kiss while the taxi drove away.

When Dan returned that evening he carried in his arms a huge bouquet of white orchids. "Do you have a large vase for these flowers?" he called.

"Oh my God, they are so beautiful." I took a deep breath and extended my arms to receive them. He walked closer to me and stood face to face until the flowers were the only things between us. He brought his face forward and kissed me for a long moment. I found myself relaxing in his arms. Slowly, he let go of the flowers and one by one they fell to the floor. Pressing himself even closer, he kissed me again. I closed my eyes and felt the heat of our embrace coursing through my body and pushing back my resistance. When we finally pulled apart, we stood looking at each other and savored this moment of closeness. We bent to pick up the flowers from the floor still silently enjoying the taste of our recent connection. Perhaps this really was a new beginning.

One by one, I arranged the flowers in a vase. Something good was beginning to take place in me and I let out a sigh of relief. Dan nodded his head lovingly. "Me, too," he whispered. "I want you to know that no matter what happens… know that I love you." He held me close again and caressed my face as you caress a fragile child's face.

All felt safe and open between us. I was to later discover, however, that the next four days would be the most deceptive in my life. While I was building new fantasies of hope in my mind and a sincere desire to develop our relationship on new grounds, Dan was planning his departure from this world. Some of the following information I later learned from friends and the police.

December 6, 1970

Outside it was a beautiful, crisp and cool morning. The last rain had washed the city and the sweet smell of flowers filled the air. Many people opened their windows and sat on their porches to enjoy the clean fresh air. "I have to attend a press conference in an hour," Dan said, and left home at 11:30 a.m., after reading the morning newspaper and having a light breakfast. "I will call you later." He kissed me and whispered gently, "Take care of yourself for me." He made his way toward the front door and closed it quietly behind him.

In truth there was no press conference. I found out later that he had wanted to take time to write a final letter to be found after his death. He walked into his office and closed the door behind him. Clearing his desk of any unnecessary papers, he moved his typewriter to the far left corner of the desk. He opened the middle drawer and pulled out a fresh writing pad, took his red ink pen and placed it carefully on the clean page. Next, he picked up the telephone on his desk and asked his secretary not to forward any calls. He walked to the window and glanced outside. A city full of action lay below. Returning to his desk, he stood staring down at the empty page. Finally, he sat down, held the pen in his hand for a brief moment and started writing. His last wishes were simple. His handwriting was neat and extremely clear. Straight lines. Word by word. Not one mistake.

He wrote the date on the top right hand side of the page and began:

December 6, 1970

To my Sara,

I cannot continue anymore. I have thought quite a lot before doing what I have done. And no one is to blame for it except myself.

I want you to know, my dear one that I loved you madly. I have thought about everything and reached a con-

clusion that this is the best and most convenient way. To sleep near my wife, after I had kissed her good night...what more could I request in my last moment?

I am happy that I was given the chance to finish thus. I did not expect more than that.

I beg your pardon for the suffering I have caused you, my Sara. I have not done it on purpose.

I spent eight wonderful years in your company. For that I cannot ever repay you.

Funny...I cannot at this moment think about anything but you although I owe much to granny, to Dad and to my family. I hope they will get over it.

At any rate, not all of them are as weak as myself. I am sorry about Granny. I hope you will help Dad to swallow the bitter pill.

I want you to marry a man who will love you.

I loved you...although I did not know, perhaps, what love is. I loved you in my way, and that has brought catastrophe upon my head.

I am simply tired. Very tired. Thirty-one years are quite enough. Every moment that you gave and every kiss is worth ten years to me.

I am going, therefore, at a ripe old age and there is no need to mourn me. Only a few are blessed with such happiness.

I know you will get over it. That is my last request from you.

You whom I loved so much.

I am leaving all I have to you. I hope you will be able to live on it decently. Perhaps the apartment in which I am leaving this world will cause some difficulties. But the monthly pension is assured. Everything is paid for even this typewriter on which I composed my work.

You don't have to sit 'Shiva' for me. I hated it in other

families, and even the Torah forbids mourning after me.

I want you to visit my grave on the anniversary until you get weary of it, of course.

Do not waste money on a tomb. I shall not feel anything more. Besides I do not want to carry a burden even after my death.

I ask for forgiveness from you, from Dad, Granny and all the others. I loved them all…in my way.

I am not afraid anymore. Since I have made up my mind, I am so tranquil.

Please put in my grave your wedding ring. Forgive me for robbing you of it, but after all, I am leaving everything else to you…and to you only.

To Sara, many tears of love.

Dan

Once he was satisfied, he gathered the pages together, folded them neatly and inserted them carefully into the envelope. He wrote on the front:

To my Sara with love

On the backside of the envelope he signed his name:

Dan

December 7, 1970

This was the day Dan planned to say a final good-bye to the people he cared for. In a strange way he felt at peace now. Finding an answer to his struggle, arriving at some clarification had a special meaning. He no longer was a victim to his pain and suffering. There was a calm in submitting to his fate. To this day, I wonder if Dan's action was a choice or a necessary act to end his battle with life, as he was driven by a force greater than himself.

Before arriving at his office he made a number of stops. He visited his father and held his hand for a long moment. "I want you to know you were always a good father to me," Dan said. As was his habitual reaction, his father did not reply at all. He rarely contributed very much to a conversation.

"I have to go," Dan continued, as he got up and went to hug his grandma in the kitchen. "I love you. I have always loved your rice… you make the best rice in the world." He smiled. She giggled, filled with joy, and hugged him back. Dan had a special affection toward his Grandma Naomi and a grateful heart for her efforts to put up with his father's controlled melancholy and gloominess.

At the editorial office he stopped by his associates to say good-bye. "I am leaving tomorrow for a long trip." He paused by Barak's office and sat with him for a few minutes. "You know, you should have my position. You are a good journalist."

"Why would you say that?" wondered Barak aloud.

"Because I've always wanted you to know how I felt about your work." He paused and added, "I'm leaving tomorrow."

"Where to?" Barak asked.

"The usual, another assignment." He paused. "This one is the mother of all assignments." He laughed and left the room.

December 8, 1970

Dan seemed to be in an especially up mood when he awoke this morning. "I had a good sleep last night," he yawned and stretched his slender body. Walking into the kitchen, he poured a cup of coffee and added with a satisfactory nod, "Lately, I seem to be sleeping well."

"That's great. I think I did, too," I said and joined him for coffee.

"It's a beautiful morning," he laughed, moving closer to me and rubbing his body next to mine. Then, suddenly, his expression changed and his face took on a gloomy, serious look. He stared at me for a long moment. "And what do you think, my love? Is it a beautiful morning?" He was still gazing at me thoughtfully.

"Why are you looking at me like that? Do you want to tell me something?"

"I just like to look at you. You are so beautiful," he added while continuing to stare. I felt uncomfortable and squirmed on the sofa. "Can't a man enjoy his wife's beauty anymore?" he laughed. "In fact, I reserved tickets for tomorrow night for us to see the National Russian Ballet at the Kameri Theater."

"How wonderful," I exclaimed.

"I knew you would like that… It is an eight o'clock show.

"There will be a cocktail party after the show and I know you'll like that, too. Wear the dress I bought you last summer in Paris."

"It's black." I didn't plan to wear a black dress. It was becoming very boring… every woman wearing her black cocktail dress. "I want to wear my long burgundy dress," I said, enchanted with the idea.

"No. The black dress." Suddenly, he became serious again and his face turned somber. He stared at me yet again, his expression loaded with a meaning I could not put my finger on. It was as if his eyes were fixed in a distance space yet they fell directly on me.

"Are you okay?" I couldn't help but asking.

"Of course… better than ever, my dear lady." His gaze still fixed on me, he continued, "As long as you take care of yourself for me. I will be thinking about you today." He got up and dressed, leaving the room with slow steps and lowering his head thoughtfully. Silently, he closed the door behind him.

December 9, 1970

Dan called me from his office at 1:45 p.m. "How are you, my lady?" He sounded content.

"I am good. I am thinking about what I should wear tonight for the ballet."

"The black dress from Paris," he replied quickly. "And don't think too much. You look beautiful in black." He did not wait for my reaction and continued, "I will be home shortly. I need to complete an important commentary for tomorrow morning's paper and I need peace and quiet. I will see you soon." Shortly thereafter I heard Dan's keys in the front door. He dropped his paperwork on the dining room table and came toward me holding out a gift box. "Open it," he said softly. "Your name was on it."

It was not out of the ordinary for Dan to surprise me with a gift, just because, and with no apparent reason at all. I opened the box carefully in great anticipation and cried out with joy, "Oh my God, it is breathtaking. It is really beautiful." There was a wide, exquisite soft gold bracelet with a heart shaped watch in its center. I pulled it out of the box and looked at it with delight. Dan took it out of my hand and placed it on my wrist.

"It is to remember all the beautiful times you have given me. I want you to wear it every day." He looked at me closely. "Now, I need you to leave, because I truly need quiet time. I need to think and to finish writing this article.

Why don't you visit your mom or a friend? All I need is a few hours." He put his hand around my shoulders and escorted me to the door. "Then we can enjoy the ballet."

"Wait. I need my jacket," I said somewhat surprised by his urgency, but I understood his need for perfection and made my way into the bedroom to grab my jacket. Dan followed me and pulled one of my sweaters out of the drawer for himself.

"I like to wear your blue cotton sweater. It is cozy," he smiled and stretched it out, pulling it down around himself to fit his body. "I like this. I am taking it away from you," he smiled again and held my hand. "And, furthermore, I don't intend to give it back to you. I'm taking it for good." He put his arm around me again and walked me toward the front door.

"Don't you want to eat something first?" I asked and moved as if to turn around.

"Oh no, I had something on my way home." He kissed me good-bye and opened the door for me.

"When should we plan on leaving for the ballet?" I asked.

"Just give me about two hours. There is plenty of time for the ballet." He smiled. I glanced at my new wristwatch. It was around 2:45 p.m. I took the elevator down to the street level and walked to my car. Raising my eyes, I saw Dan watching me from the porch. He raised his hand and waved one last good-bye.

After I left, Dan walked over to the phone and dialed the number for the taxi station nearest our home. He waited for the voice to come up on the other end and requested, "I need a taxi for 3:30 this afternoon. Please make sure the driver comes upstairs as I have a few pieces of luggage."

Dan glanced at his wristwatch and saw that it was 2:50 p.m. That gave him just enough time.

He put the receiver back in its place and pulled the envelope from the inside pocket of his jacket. Slowly, he looked at it and placed it on the dining room table. Then, he looked around and carefully rolled up the area rug in our living room and pushed it to the far corner. Looking around once more, he steadily made his way to the second bedroom and brought the gun back with him to the living room, placing it gently on the table next to the envelope. Then, he reached for the phone and for the last time called the taxi station to make sure the driver was on his way. "I need him precisely at 3:30," he said looking at his wrist-watch. In fact, you can send the driver now... tell him to come upstairs. I will need his help... apartment number 12, top floor. I will be leaving the door open. Thank you," and he put the receiver down and made his way to the kitchen. There he took the small radio from the counter top and placed it in the bathroom turning the volume up as high as it would go. He shut all the windows and unlocked the front door as he took one more glance at his wristwatch. It was just about 3:15. He took the gun and entered the bath-room. One more time, he opened the gun to make sure that all its chambers were loaded...

At 4:30, as I approached our home, I could see the police cars and the crowd hovering around outside. I stopped my car in the middle of the street, as I could not drive any far-ther due to all the people blocking the way. I got out of the car abruptly, holding my hands over my head. Inside, I could sense that something terrible had happened.

Neighbors and curious onlookers were whispering and shaking their heads in astonishment. Some were pointing their fingers at me. I heard a young man saying to the policeman, "That's her. That's Mrs. Tavor."

"Are you Mrs. Tavor?" the policeman asked, approaching me directly.

"Yes," I said choking on my words.

"I need you to come with me," he said, and gently escorted me to his car. He was extremely considerate. I asked him what had happened but he kept avoiding my question and there was no clue on his face. Finally he said, "We need to go to the station first."

We arrived at the police station and he walked me to one of the rooms where he asked me to wait patiently. "Please relax," he said noticing my agitation. A member of your family is on his way," he promised.

Sitting in the cold waiting room, I was afraid that the worst had happened. Thoughts were flying around my head, so vivid, yet confused. Had I been fooled? Was I losing my mind? Just two days ago we had returned from a long weekend in Eilat, a second honeymoon for our new beginning. And what about the tickets to the ballet for this evening? What about Dan's positive mood over this past week? Things were not adding up and I was hoping to be awakened from this nightmare.

Finally, the door opened and a policewoman walked in. Behind her were my Uncle Abraham and our friend Barak. Our eyes met and they both walked in closer to me. Uncle Abraham took my hand, looked at me kindly and said the words. "Dan has killed himself." He opened his arms and I fell into them.

After a moment, I pulled away and asked, "Is he okay?" I knew I did not make sense but I couldn't seem to let in the reality.

"Listen, Sara," Barak interrupted shaking my shoulders lightly as if he wished to awaken me. "He killed himself," he repeated very clearly. There was no hesitation in his voice. He appeared stronger than ever. I opened my mouth but could not find the words. Instead, my body dropped into a close by chair. I felt overwhelmed with a multitude of feelings ranging from grief to anger. I heard myself breathing deeply with a sigh of relief. It was an uncontrollable sigh. It was over. I felt embarrassed and wished to vanish, to curl in on myself, to shrink into the very chair I was sitting on.

Barak shrugged his shoulders. He could not understand. How could he? He did not live in my body nor did he sleep in my bed. Yes, he knew about our life together but only what we allowed him to see. He could not know about the yelling and the degradation. He could not know about the nights I lay next to my husband and prayed he would not reach for me. Barak came closer and whispered, "Dan loved you…" He paused and waited for my reaction. I was silent.

He could not have loved me, I thought. *He did not even think I was worth living for. How could he have loved me?*

Time seemed to stop. Barak moved away and looked at my Uncle Abraham. I heard him saying, "She will be okay. She is a strong lady."

At that moment a tall, burly, mustached cop walked into the room with my Aunt Doris. She rushed into the room almost pushing the policeman aside. Looking back and forth between Uncle Abraham and me, she exclaimed, "Good God, I just heard about it… Who would have thought? He was so young… Yet, who knew what went on between the two of them," she whispered loudly to

Abraham.

"I don't know," Abraham replied, "but for now, I need you to take her to Mom's house. Barak and I have to go to Dan's father right now to deliver the dreadful news... I don't know how we are going to do that." With that, they left the room and I remained with Aunt Doris, following the policeman down the corridor to the exit door. We left with our heads down.

On the way back to my grandmother's home, Doris could not stop talking. "It is already in the news; it is already the talk of the city... We should take a taxi and get the hell out of here." Outside the police station, Doris lifted her hand and called a taxi. As we crawled into the back seat, she was still carrying on. "Everyone is talking, gossiping about what has just happened. It is going to be in the morning paper tomorrow. It is terrible... The poor man. Why should he end up like this? Dan was a good man... everyone loved him. He had a great future ahead of him... What a loss for the family. What a loss for you... You know that a taxi driver found his body lying on the floor in your apartment around 3:30... and he was the one that called the police... Lucky you didn't return earlier to see him... The driver said he asked him to come upstairs... He loved you so much... everyone knows that. So what could be so bad about that? Why would he want to kill himself?" She didn't wait for an answer and I did not plan on giving her one. "I just wonder what made him kill himself," she repeated. "I don't understand. Who can understand or believe this? A man like Dan. I don't understand..." Pointing her finger at me, she finally burst out, "What the hell did you do to make him kill himself?"

"Stop it! Stop it already," I yelled and finally broke my silence with obvious rage. My eyes were dry and all I felt was a burning deep down in my heart. Anger and bitterness took hold of me. I don't even think I heard everything Doris was saying. I remember her mouth and lips moving quickly as if she was chewing food. Suddenly, I felt nauseous.

The cab driver stopped his taxi abruptly in front of my grandmother's house and I left Doris behind as quickly as possible.

I entered my grandmother's house with Doris behind me. I could see many members of the family and close friends clustered around in small groups. As I walked in, they stopped talking and I collapsed onto the first chair in the room. Inside my heart there was a feeling of apprehension and fear of what Doris had accused me of. Was it my fault? "It is always the woman's fault," Dan had once said.

Debbie, Barak's wife, walked toward me and sat down in the adjacent chair. "I am sorry Sara… I am so sorry and so angry. I wish I could bring him back just in order to kill him again for what he has done to you… it is horrible!" and she put her arms around me.

"You are a good friend, Debbie… you and Barak are the best," I said quietly. "I am suddenly very, very tired."

Quietly, I got up and walked toward my grandma's bedroom. Their eyes followed me as I closed the door behind me and climbed into bed. Finally, the tears came as I curled into myself hugging the pillow tight and burying my face away from my future.

CHAPTER 18

Respect for the Dead

What doesn't kill me makes me stronger.
—Albert Camus

As I wrapped my body around the pillow trying to escape and ignore the obvious whispering in my Grammy's living room, Barak and Uncle Abraham were just approaching the home of Dan's father. It was already after 9:30 at night. Heavy, dark clouds covered the city and spread out like an umbrella over their heads. They reached the front door and stood silently for a long moment before finally knocking.

"Who is it?" They could hear the old man's deep voice on the other side of the door.

"Barak. It's Barak and Abraham," Barak called out with an effort. Gadi, Dan's younger brother, opened the door. The old man and Dan's grandma were standing behind him; their faces were cold and filled with worried anticipation.

"What's happened?" the old man called with obvious panic at the unusual visit.

"Come in. Come in," said Gadi inviting the two men inside. "So what is it? What's happened?" Gadi continued, his voice becoming a little anxious.

"It's about Dan," Barak replied.

"Yes, what's happened to Dan?" the father queried, moving his hand with a nervous flurry.

"Sir, he's shot himself." Barak spoke firmly and directly at the father, saying it as clearly as he could. He left no room for doubt.

Dan's father let out a cry and reared back as if something had struck him, raising his hands in the air and slapping his chest. Barak and Abraham rushed to calm him but he pushed them away with all his might. He kept hitting his chest as if to attack his pain and grief, until Gadi got hold of him and cried, "Stop. Stop it!" Gadi continued talking while trying to help his father compose himself. "Listen to me, Dad… It's okay." Gadi spoke with surprising control and restraint. "It's okay… this is what my brother chose for himself and we," he gestured with his hand to everyone in the room, "should honor his will! We should honor his will and not cry like old women."

As he spoke, Grammy's weeping voice penetrated from the far corner of the room where she sat curled on the floor holding her knees and burying her head in her lap. She kept up a steady wail that was disconcerting and hard to ignore. Dan's father glared at her and aimed his anger in her direction shouting, "Let her cry… Let the bitch cry! She needs to cry for the kind of daughter she gave birth to… Let her cry for the rest of her life… I have to put up with her face every day… I have to feed her every day. It's good that she cries."

Barak and Abraham could not understand why the

father threw his rage onto the old lady as neither one of them knew about the escape of Dan's mother back to Baghdad and her lover. The old lady was a steady reminder of her daughter. There was a silent confusion that permeated the room and the father suddenly realized that his behavior might reveal the family secret about his wife. Gadi hushed his father and then turned his attention toward Granny. He sat on the floor next to her cradling her with sympathy.

"Granny, there is no need to cry. Really, Dan would not want you to cry... It was his will and we have to respect his will," he kept repeating to the great surprise of Barak and Uncle Abraham. They both looked at each other in bewilderment, trying to understand and accept Gadi's logic.

It was too much for Abraham to believe and he could not help but ask the young man, "Did you have any idea at all that Dan... I mean did he ever mention anything like this to you as a possibility?"

Before Gadi could say anything his father interfered. "Dan had no reason in the world to kill himself as long as he was with us... But since he's gotten married, your family had him. He hardly came here anymore... He hardly came to visit me, his father... You took him away from us... Your niece took him away from us." He pointed his finger at my uncle with rage. "She took him away from me and this is the result!" His face turned red and his hands trembled above his head. "That's what brought this disaster."

"Father! That's really enough." Gadi sent a quick look at my uncle who was standing there dumbfounded, frozen in his place. "He is not in his right mind now... He does not know what he is talking about... Really, forgive him."

Gadi was very anxious to contain his father. "Please, Father, just be quiet. This is enough."

It was too uncomfortable for the visitors to stay any longer and Barak shuffled his feet looking for the right moment to excuse himself. Finally, he said, "I guess we'll be on our way now… The funeral is tomorrow at 2:00 p.m." Barak turned to Uncle Abraham and they both silently left.

When they returned to my Grandma Sophie's home, I could hear their talking through the wall. "The brother's reaction was a surprising one," Barak commented.

"Yes, but the father was blaming us and…" Uncle Abraham said.

"He is a bitter old man," Barak interrupted. "I wouldn't worry about it, Abe," he spoke with reassurance.

"What did he say?" Doris inquired.

Abraham shrugged his shoulders, "You don't want to know. He is blaming everyone," he continued, looking around the room. "The shocking part was his rage against the old woman blaming her for his misfortune… How can he blame her for her daughter's death? I don't understand." He turned toward Barak as if requesting an answer. "The poor woman."

"So what did he say?" Doris repeated again fishing for details.

"It's really not so important right now… Everyone should get some sleep," Grandma Sophie interjected in an attempt to put an end to the gossip. Debbie was quick to agree.

"I sent Sara off to get some sleep. She seemed very weak and overwhelmed as if she needed to be taken care of. It is a fragile time for her." Debbie turned toward her husband and added, "I think it's time for us to leave. We will see you all at the cemetery tomorrow."

I heard the door close and immediately tightened my grip on the pillow as if something was being snatched out of my body. I felt a special bond and closeness to Debbie and Barak at that moment. Their presence was soothing. They seemed to be the only ones I could draw some compassion and thoughtfulness from. When they left, I felt a dryness in my mouth and wanted to throw up. I shut my eyes tight, making an effort to close out the world around me. The night wore on and I tried restlessly to sleep. How I hungered for the morning sun to shine again and with it for everything to return to normal.

The next day we all went to the cemetery. The last farewell for Dan was a day fit to remember, a day that set the tone for the rest of my life. It stayed with me like the smoke from a fire that continued to burn and smolder. Barak's presence at the funeral was vital and he was to become my lifeline for years to come. I kept his comments and encouragement close to my heart. I never forgot his statement that I had added eight extra years to Dan's life.

I used to think of it often along with Dan's final letter that I learned to repeat to myself word for word. It became my personal mantra for many years to come. Sometimes, I shared it with others who were willing to listen. I think I shared it in order to convince myself that I was free to be.

I especially recall Momo's reaction, my mother's newlywed husband. He stretched his chest and said wisely, "I agree with Barak one hundred percent. Take it from a man's point of view. You added to Dan's life years of joy."

The day after the funeral I had to go back to my home and face the void that Dan had left. My mother and sister would join me later just before the rest of the family and friends were to arrive for the Shiva but, in the meantime, I was alone. I turned the key in the door and pushed it open with my angry body. At first glance I could not recognize my own home. The coffee table was full of cigarette butts from the investigation, some in the ashtray and some on the table. The top of the table was scribbled all over with a red marker. Newspapers were on the floor and cigarette ashes were all over the sofa. The area rug was folded and pushed to the end of the room. I noticed a small plastic bag of red sand lying on Dan's armchair.

I felt cold and empty in my own body. Folding my arms, I leaned against the wall, slowly scanning the room with my eyes. There was a smudge of blood in the entry between the living room and the hallway. I closed my eyes, thinking that maybe I had better wait for my mom and sister outside. Taking careful steps, I made my way toward the front door and walked outside. I could not help but notice the red sand to the right of the steps… that's where Dan must have gathered the sand that was in the plastic bag… but for what purpose? Dan was not a believer nor was he superstitious. In fact, he did not believe in anything, not even in himself… and yet, he had gathered red sand. "From earth we come and to earth we shall return?"

I ground my teeth and bitterly ran back inside, grabbed the bag of sand and threw it all over the living room. As my wounded self cried, I took one object after another and threw them to the floor, watching them smash into tiny pieces. I grabbed the old newspapers and crushed them in my hands, throwing them far into the room as if they were small paper balls. Fury kindled my energy and I continued to wail, kicking Dan's favorite armchair in frustration. The door opened and my mother and sister stood still there gaping.

"My God, what has happened to you?" my mom exclaimed. "We should not have let her come on her own." She started picking up the items from the floor and my sister brought in the broom to sweep. "People will be here any moment," my mom thought out loud with concern. "What is that red sand on the floor? She pointed with her hand toward my sister to sweep up the sand as fast as possible.

I slowly walked toward Dan's armchair and dropped my body into it. Bending down and picking up the newspaper from the floor, I saw that it was yesterday's. On the front page was Dan's happy smile beaming up at me. Under his picture I read the first few lines in large print.

Dan Tavor, the noted writer and commentator has committed suicide. Was this member of the most cynical profession moved to take his own life by the betrayal of his wife? Or, was the tragedy caused by the shadow of his political life?

Trying to make sense of Dan's final act was an ongoing effort. It was a mystery to myself and others, and the speculation swirled around fast even from the very first day. I held the paper in my hands and tore it to little pieces, leaving only Dan's picture, and laid it on the coffee table in front of me.

"What are you doing?" my mom asked, noticing my actions.

"I thought maybe he would like to be with us at the Shiva," I laughed bitterly.

"Stop that… it is not respectful," she said and removed the picture from the table.

"Respectful?" I yelled in a rage. "I tell you I am sick and tired of hearing about respect… respect this and respect that. Honor this and honor that when in fact everyone is spilling dirt in everyone's face every day. No one gives a damn… such hypocrisy… besides, if I were you, I would not mention the word respect!" I did not care how hard I hit. She glanced at me with deep sorrow and kept silent.

"It is not good for you to be angry like that," I heard my sister, Rechel, speaking under her breath.

"I am asking you to respect the dead, not me," my mother said.

I could not help but laugh and mock her comment.

"Respect the dead? And what about the living?" I asked her bitterly. I did not expect an answer and did not get one. My sister buried herself in the cleaning as if she was trying to clean the hurt, the guilt and the shame. As I looked back and forth between the two of them, I kept quiet.

"Some people are starting to come," my sister cried looking out on the porch and rushing to pick up her sweeping.

Aunt Doris walked in first, wrapping her hand around her husband's arm. Barak and his wife, Debbie, looked straight in my direction and Debbie made her way over to sit next to me. Gideon, Dan's friend and my grand aunt's son, followed them. He looked at me and put his hand on his heart, a sign of sympathy and kindness. Another of Dan's friends from work, Deborah, walked in with a pile of magazines and newspapers, which she left with my mother. I heard her say, "Keep these for later. There are articles about Dan." My brother, Carmel, showed up in his paratrooper uniform as this was his first year in the service. But the strangest visitor was Dan's night editor when he walked in with obvious anger. He walked quickly into the living room and strode over toward me.

"I am so sorry I did not attend the funeral yesterday…

I could not bear to see him buried six feet under… I simply can't understand him. To say the least I am angry with him." He took a deep breath to regain his calm. People had hushed and were listening to him. "Look, look at this," he said and pulled up his sleeve exposing a serial number tattooed on his arm. "I went through the concentration camps. I ate rotten potatoes… I slept with corpses… I looked like a corpse myself. But never, never did I think of taking my own life. I never thought of suicide." He looked around the room.

There was deep silence and an uneasy feeling circulating in the air. His rage was making people uncomfortable. Besides, the rabbi was due at any moment. He took my hand in his palm and concluded, "Forgive me, Sara, but I refuse to sit Shiva for him… I refuse to acknowledge his action… this is sheer madness… sheer madness… a waste of a good life. I just stopped by to pay my condolences to you." He had made his point very clear and he now seemed to be relieved. "I should go now. Mrs. Tavor, if you need anything at all, please let me know." I said nothing, but admired his courage. I watched him turn around and leave the room.

There was a short silence after he left but people kept on arriving and he was soon forgotten. I suppose some agreed with him but most found him too extreme, too direct. People don't like to talk about suicide and the sooner you close the lid on such a matter the better it is.

Most of the people knew Dan but they were only acquaintances to me. I noticed that my father did not show up. He was not at the funeral nor do I remember hearing from him afterwards. I guess he did not want to be a part of my bad luck.

The rabbi arrived and after acknowledging me, he

began the prayer. During the seven days of the Shiva I was numb and detached. I felt sorry for my family and regretted that somehow I had failed them. It felt like I was being cut down and reduced to a point of no return. I was powerless because I could not turn the clock back and undo Dan's death. I was immobilized because I couldn't find the words to make a difference in my life and in the lives of my loved ones. I felt like every word I uttered and every move I made was inspected like a moth under a magnifying glass. When I wasn't seething with anger, I felt that I had to surrender to what was now. I had to accept the road that Dan had coursed for me.

Friends and some members of the family behaved as if there was no history or feeling between us. There seemed to be a denial of reality. Was it a survival mechanism, or fear that my unenviable position could be contagious? In any case, I was no longer considered a member of the winning team. It is only in looking back that I can write about this period of my life. I could not see it at the time. I believe that my denial was my protector and my guardian, since if I had seen their rejection and their prejudice at that time, perhaps I would not have been able to survive. Of course, I had a glimpse of it but quickly dismissed the possibility of being rejected and accused by my own friends and family.

At the end of the seven days people stopped showing up at my home, with the exception of my sister, brothers and mother, who by her actions made a most profound amends to me. She still came out with remarks I did not know what to do with, but for the most part she was there for me and honored my presence with compassion. I spent many hours at her home where she catered to me. She was very careful not to mention Dan's name or to ask too many questions about my past or my plans for the future. She gave me all the space I needed and more. It was like coming back to the home I had never had with her. She cooked and cleaned and never asked for me to help her. I felt her love and could see the sorrow in her eyes for what I was going through even though she made a great effort to hide it from me. I rarely saw Aunt Doris, although Uncle Abraham used to stop by my mom's on his way to work to see how everyone was doing. My sister and I remained close and she became my lifeline in the years to come. I tried to keep the connection with my friends and the rest of the family, but it was different now. It seemed that Dan took with him all the significant relationships we had had. With Dan's absence I became an outcast. The phone hardly rang and the invitations stopped coming. The sparkling world of Cinderella became a thing of the past. I knew I had to plan a new life for myself but did not know where to start.

One early morning after I had returned home, the doorbell rang. I jumped as I was still filled with apprehension. It was a loud and piercing ring. At the door stood a man in his late thirties, his broad shoulders almost blocking the doorway. His hair was meticulously combed and his blue striped shirt was buttoned up neatly. He opened his mouth pushing his thick moustache away from the corners of his lips.

"Mrs. Tavor?" he asked and his eyes searched mine.

I nodded my head ready for anything.

"I am the police sergeant who conducted the inquiry into your husband's death." He nodded his head looking into the living room. "May I come in?" He walked in not waiting for my reply.

"Sorry if my men left a mess here. They had to investigate every possibility and, of course, we were in a hurry. The funeral you know… I know they don't clean up after themselves very well," he laughed although it did not seem very genuine. "I am here about the gun. You are Mrs. Tavor, aren't you?" He wanted to make sure as he noticed the startled look on my face.

"Yes, I am." I moved back out of his way as he was walking around the room as if still looking for something.

"It's all right… we closed the case," he smiled and rested his heavy hand on my shoulder in a too familiar way. "But I am here about the gun," he repeated. "I would like to buy it from you." He spilled his words out as fast as he could.

"But, I don't have it," I said intently.

"Oh, I know, of course. It's in our possession… but still you own it… as you inherited all your husband's possessions and that was one of them. He paid a dear price for it." His eyes moved around the room as if he was estimating the value of every item. "It is a good gun. One of the most expensive handguns one could carry," he commented thoughtfully. And then, he moved his palm over a nearby standing lamp and added in an attempt to change the mood, "This must be an antique piece. It is very beautiful." But, he quickly turned his glance back at me as he was really only after the gun—that vile instrument with which Dan had removed himself from this world.

I tried to imagine how this steel weapon had moved in Dan's long thin fingers. How had it been loaded? Who had forced the issue, Dan or the gun? I later heard that Dan had aimed the shot at the crown of his head as he probably did not wish to spoil his looks.

Now, I owned this gun. Now, I could have some money

for it. I silently smiled at the irony of this world of ours. A new gun that had taken only one life, I reflected almost hysterically and could not help but let out a sound of mockery in my voice. "Sir, I'll tell you what. You can have it. It will be my gift to you… if you promise not to use it again… One life is all this gun was meant to take." I regained some confidence and sat down in the nearest chair waiting for the sergeant's answer.

He removed his glasses and scratched his head with a strained smile on his face. "That is very kind of you, Mrs. Tavor… but I can't make such a promise. Guns are meant to protect, of course, but they are also meant to kill. This is a very hard proposition." He smiled now.

"Well… what do you say?" I did not let go and held his eyes in a steady gaze.

"Actually, I have a service revolver given to me by the police, but I do not want to be attached to the police force anymore… I would like to have a gun of my own… After all, it is a good gun." He tried to hide the enthusiasm that had crept into his voice.

Sure it is a good gun, I thought, *all it took was one pull of the trigger to blow out Dan's life… and mine.*

He quickly glanced at me and said with renewed energy as if he had just found the answer. "Well… I tell you what, Mrs. Tavor… I promise!"

"You do?" I was surprised.

"Yes, I promise to use this gun for protection only."

I stared into his eyes and noticed they were cold and uncertain… I had no way of knowing what runs through a policeman's mind… besides, what did I expect? After all, what kind of a request was I making?

"Then it's settled?" He hurried on to say, "I shall bring

you the transfer form tomorrow." He seemed most grateful, and made his way to the door asking me not to get up. "It's okay. I can close the door behind me." But, on second thought, he turned around, saying in good sprits, "I thank you, Mrs. Tavor, and I want you to know that I am really sorry for your loss. It is a great mystery why a man in Mr. Tavor's position would do what he did."

I sat in my chair perfectly still and watched him close the door behind him. But I could not close the door behind Dan's death, nor did people let me.

CHAPTER 19

Gossip

No sword bites so fiercely as an evil tongue.
—Sir Philip Sidney

At night, sometimes I could hear Dan's footsteps, his usual shuffling walk. My body would lay there tense and I would follow the sound with absolute stillness. I was not afraid, as I knew Dan loved me and he would never harm me. I only wished to know if it was my imagination playing tricks on me, or perhaps it happened because I longed so much to talk with him. I would lay for many hours in confusion and wake up the next morning feeling tired and restless.

It had now been a couple of weeks since Dan's funeral. I was tired of my own misery and was aware of my tendency to dip my soul in the tears of self-pity. I understood that my well-being was on the line and that I was losing the power to survive and triumph over my tragedy. I was determined to lift up my head and remove the veil of apathy. Finally, I went searching for an apartment to rent in the outskirts of Tel Aviv, a new place where I could find respite from my memories.

I chose the broker nearest to me. It was only a few blocks away from my home and as I walked into the office, I was shown into the waiting room by a tall, attractive, young girl. She looked about my age. "Boss'll be free in a minute," she said glancing at my clothes and smiling. "Is black back in fashion again?" She did not wait for my answer and disappeared into the hallway. I sat down and flipped idly through a magazine.

An argument broke out from behind the closed door between a client and the broker. The voice of a young woman was angrily yelling that the apartment he offered her was not in accordance with her stipulations. Finally, she left the office threatening to sue him. He reacted with a big guffaw and ambled out of his office to the waiting room.

"Did you hear that?" he asked the girl at the front desk. "She signed the contract before seeing the apartment. In the meantime, I succeeded in leasing the apartment to an old tourist for a better price. I gave her another apartment just as good... only a few blocks down the street... how bad is that? Now, she is shouting at me trying to sue me... Ha... let her sue me if she's got the money to spend!" He smiled, revealing uneven teeth behind his mustache. He opened the door to his office and invited me in. "Now, let's see, how can I help you? What is your name?"

"Sara. My name is Sara and I am looking for a one bedroom apartment outside of Tel Aviv," I said following him into his office.

"Why outside of Tel Aviv? Is Tel Aviv so bad?" he laughed and brushed his mustache with his thumb. When I avoided his question, he looked down at his pile of papers and began to read my application. He then lifted up his head.

"People think I am an advertising pillar. They come to me to get an immediate answer. They never tell me their reasons... as if I am forbidden to show interest in my fellow man." He separated the papers and ran his finger across it, skimming as he talked. "Sometimes I can help..." He looked at me and stuck his fingernail between his teeth to clean them. "You are too quiet. Say something... Here is one in Givataim," he finally concluded pulling a form from his drawer. "Sign here," he said.

"I'd like to see what you have first before I sign," I said, recalling the anger of the last client.

"Why are you so hard to please? You seem in a bad mood... Tell me, why are you leaving Tel Aviv? All the young people love to be in Tel Aviv and you want to leave." His insolent prying into my affairs made me lose my patience. I got up and walked toward the door.

"Wait, wait a minute... I am sure I have something for you." He attempted to detain me with the urgency in his voice. I paused and waited. "Do you live nearby?" he asked in a friendly tone now.

"Yes, not too far... on Sokolov Street," I said. My answer brought a new spirit into his face for he folded his paper and raised his eyebrow, moving anxiously in his chair.

"Then you must have heard about the newspaperman. He lived on the same street... He committed suicide recently."

I stared at him and could not help but notice his wide-open mouth. His moustache moved upward. His dirty teeth were full of tobacco bits. He looked at me again searching my reaction intuitively. His hand had gone up to the nape of his neck and he scratched his ear in satisfaction.

"I used to read his stuff… He had published a new book not too long ago… I am sure you heard of him," he insisted still examining me closely.

"Umm… I haven't heard… no," I lied poorly.

"How come you haven't heard? It is the talk of the town… you probably live on the same block. Sokolov Street is a very small street. This is a very small city!" He demanded an answer, and all I wanted to do was to disappear from the face of the earth.

"I heard his wife was the cause… I heard she was a good piece of work. Oh, you women…"

I felt my anger building up and I did not mind staying around to clear my name. "Why do you think she was the cause?" I asked with some bravery.

"Of course she was the cause… Why else would a man like him take his life? I heard she betrayed him with his best friend… so he took his life. He should have killed her instead!" He pointed his finger in the air in absolute conviction. Leaning back on his chair, he reached for his cigarette pack offering me one.

"No thanks." I shook my head staring straight at him.

He lit his cigarette and looked at me behind his smoke. "Dan Tavor…Yes… Dan Tavor, that was his name." He raised his finger close to his head in triumph.

I looked at him for a long moment… a small man… little less than a boy… who had done the only thing he knew how to do well. Play with people's lives. An empty life I thought or perhaps he, too, had a role to fulfill? He played a judge of mankind. I could see him trying to put all the pieces together, sizing me up and down.

I moved to go saying, "I have to leave now… I will stop

by for the apartment later on." I needed to save myself while I still could.

"No. No, please wait… I have only one more question." He got up from his chair and leaned on the front of his desk. "What did you say your name was?" He was ready for the kill. "Of course, Sara. I read the paper. You are his wife," he burst into an ugly laugh. "I should have guessed it from the very beginning… you are wearing black." He shook his head with some pleasure. "And you wish to move out of Tel Aviv. I can find a good place for you… I understand you leaving town… people talking… I understand now. Of course everything makes sense now." He tapped his left hand on his desk while still talking. "I heard you have a nice apartment. Are you selling it, renting it? I can help, you know," he laughed again.

Something detained me. I stayed glued to my place; my hands and feet weighed heavily as if they were made of lead. I watched this short, ugly man moving closer. Possibly I was absorbed by my own feeling of pain… an unusual sharp sensation in my heart… I was viewing the ugly side of a human being that needed to hurt. Impaled by the broker's mocking voice, I waited to view my own misery.

"They say he loved you… so why did you betray him… you wanted more loving? More sex? He did not give enough?" He bit his lower lip, obviously gloating over the lurid picture that conjured up in his mind. He left his desk and moved toward me. I was frightened now. Feeling dryness in my mouth, I was trembling and a cold sweat covered my body. I had a strong desire to vomit. I think I murmured Dan's name as I used to do when getting into a difficult spot. All I wanted to do at that moment was to perish. I looked at the gloating face of the broker. It seemed

wider and bigger than before, moving back and forth slowly. He grabbed my arm. His face filled with a sickly pleasure and he began whispering loquacious words of passion.
"If you did it once, you can do it again. I can give you real
good loving… come here, baby," and he pulled me forward
toward his open, gaping mouth and tightened his grip on
my arm.

My fear turned into anger as I drew my arm strongly
away from his hold and pushed him away with all my
might. I was surprised to see him stagger back. "You putting up a fight? I like that," he said, composing himself
quickly. "But, don't think you can play smart with me." He
threw his body at me, laying his hand on the wall above my
head and brought his face close to mine. I felt his heavy
breath on my cheek and smelled the strong aroma of bad
tobacco. "So you like to play with me, baby," he whispered
filling me with revulsion. I shut my eyes and awaited the
impossible. I pushed myself back as if I wanted to move the
walls away, slid down and freed myself. He let me go and
remained standing with his face to the wall, his hand still
supporting his stocky body. Explosively, he slammed the
wall with his hand as I ran to the exit door, pulling the handle strongly. I heard his laughter again when I could not
open the door. He turned his body and grabbed my hands.
"Look, you should read," he pointed with his finger at the
word above the handle saying PUSH. I threw a last frightened look at him and pushed the door open. I was out of
the building and into the fresh air as fast as my legs could
carry me.

Something precious in me had been shattered. The broker's laughter killed it as surely as a bullet would have. I
have heard that the one who kills himself dies once, but the

survivor dies a hundred times. My visit to the broker had definitely been one of those deaths.

But, the stronger I was hit, the stronger my will to survive became. One night, after ten o'clock, my neighbor who lived up above knocked on my door. She was an old maid with a small puppy, who had a mini telescope on her porch. Mrs. Swagman was her name but everyone called her "the pink lady" for she had bright pink hair and her skin was pale and full of goose bumps. She always walked slowly and could be seen with her puppy. I was very surprised to see her for we had never spoken a word, except maybe for a brief hello and exchange of polite smiles. Now, she stood in front of my door, holding her puppy close to her heart, stroking his fur. "Mrs. Tavor, I noticed that your mail box is full." She peered over my shoulder into my living room.

"Thank you, I will get it first thing tomorrow morning," I said with appreciation.

"Oh, you have a nice home," she said, moving forward and gently putting her puppy on the floor. The little white dog wagged his tail and ran into the living room as if he was reading "the pink lady's" mind. "Oh, I'm sorry… I will get him. Come here. Come here to mommy." She ran after him into my apartment and picked him up stroking his fur. "I am so sorry, Mrs. Tavor."

"That's all right. A cute dog," I said.

She glanced at me pleasantly. "You are a nice girl." Then she added in a whispering tone, "I want to ask you something. What was all the arguing about between the two of you? I used to hear you crying… Were you close to a divorce?" I was surprised to hear her question. "You know, he loved you. He was always bringing you flowers…

and that could have been a hard thing for him to swallow." She kept on patting her dog with quick movements. I moved back and was ready to escort her out the door when she went on to justify her visit. "Oh listen, Mrs. Tavor. It really is none of my business, but someone must tell you that they are all gossiping about you. You know the nature of people… I myself am very fond of you. You are so young and beautiful. It could happen to anyone. I mean… wanting a divorce. I myself never got married… Once they marry you, they own you!" She spoke on softly in a friendly manner that I found difficult to trust. I made an effort to keep my mouth shut and finally closed the door leaving "the pink lady" outside. I heard her murmuring to herself as she shuffled down the hallway, "Strong girl… such a strong girl."

And yet, I didn't always feel like a "strong girl." One more time I was plagued with doubts about the divorce and why Dan had actually killed himself. In my mind I could not and did not want to understand Dan's action. To me, nothing could justify suicide. I kept looking for clues. His last note to me seemed to be the closest and so I held onto it for a long time. After all, he did say, "No one is to blame but myself." But in reality, his entire note was as much of a mystery as his own death. His explanation about dying at a ripe old age was merely philosophical. Perhaps, for him it was the only valid way to look at life, but for me it explained nothing.

Two weeks after Dan's burial I heard from Gadi, Dan's younger brother. "I understand that Dan left a note for you," he said in a calm and direct voice. "I'd like to read it… In return, you can read my note from him.

"Oh Gadi, it is good to hear from you," I exclaimed as

I was truly happy he had called. Unfortunately, this was more than I received back.

"Yes, likewise…" and then there was a silence on the other end of the line. He was waiting to hear my reply.

"Certainly… of course you can read my note… any time," I said.

The next day at 4:00 p.m., I opened the front door. Gadi stood there leaning on the doorframe and holding the envelope in his hand. "Come in," I invited him quietly. He walked in briskly and sat in Dan's armchair. In a business-like manner he waited for me to exchange the notes. For a split second I feared handing my envelope to him before receiving his. I was still not very trusting and not sure of Gadi's intentions anymore.

What if he took my letter and would not give it back? What if he took it and left? That would be as if I lost Dan one more time because his note to me was the only link I had to him now. That piece of paper could prove my inno-cence. It was the only tangible and meaningful expression of his thoughts toward me. How desperate I felt in my loss. I had lost Dan and I realized in turn I was losing myself, my spirit, my trust, my essence. It was too high a price to pay.

Reluctantly, I handed the envelope to Gadi and he gave me his. The note that Dan had left Gadi was shorter, less than a page in length and written in a clear and strangely calm tone as if Dan was writing a post card from the beau-tiful mountains of Greece. Like my note there was no sense of panic or fear. Here, too, Dan asked that no one be blamed for his action, and indicated his love to all the members of his family. He ended it with a final good-bye.

Gadi was still reading when I carefully folded the note

and inserted it back into its envelope. Finally, Gadi lifted his head and with no emotion at all he handed me my note. To my surprise, he made no comment at all and with a clear lack of the significance of our meeting, at least in my eyes, he stood up ready to leave. "Thank you," he said throwing a last glance around the room.

"That was Dan's favorite chair," I said with a slow smile, pointing to Gadi's empty seat. He glanced at the armchair and laughed an abrupt laugh.

"Not important anymore is it?" he shrugged his shoulders. He made his way out and closed the door behind him. That was the last time I ever saw Gadi.

Slowly, I had to accept the fact that not only had Dan deserted me but everyone else was now choosing to leave me as well. Sometimes my conflicted anger would take on a new slant, viewing Dan as weak. Weak and cold, and not able to take charge of his life and problems. Just as I felt I was now being judged so I, in turn, judged Dan.

"No doubt Dan's action indicated weakness and a lack of appreciation for life's beauty. Who would do such a thing?" I said to whomever was willing to listen. "No matter what the problem… suicide should not be the solution," I stated in building my case. I myself started to believe in my theory and to draw some strength and satisfaction from it. "He was running away from the problem rather than challenging it. That is a cowardly and fearful way of handling life." I was determined to demonstrate to myself and others that Dan's loss had no affect on me and so I continued to blame him.

But, strangely enough, as I continued to point the finger, I also continued to idealize him and focused on the good times we had had. I pictured Dan as having a heroic personality, someone with above average talent. My endless contradictions seemed to be a good way to manage and cope with my suffering.

Everyone else appeared to have their own version of the story—each satisfying a need within them. The papers said it was too much success too quickly. He was in a "constant philosophical struggle with life." My Uncle Abraham believed that Dan perhaps had been involved in a military act or some sort of espionage and that his death was only staged as a suicide. "After all, why would he go on so many different trips on his own?" he wondered. "Turkey and Yugoslavia… those are not countries you tour for fun. It is not like he went to Paris or Rome. And why would the police say that it had been planned like a military operation? It's possible," he said. "After all Dan was no ordinary man!"

Frankly, it seemed too far-fetched to me and I never gave his idea much attention.

On the other hand, Deborah, Dan's associate, believed that Dan's life and death would remain an unsolved mystery forever. She kept on saying, "We will never know for certain… His death is a riddle to me." She kept one of his pictures next to her bedside. "I never want to forget him." On one of her visits to my apartment she advised me to seek therapy saying that this was not a simple thing to get over. I remember her words very clearly. "Do yourself a favor and listen to me," she repeated. "Get some therapy." She could tell I was not very open to her proposal. Deborah lifted her briefcase ready to leave. She glanced at me one more time and added, "Listen, just think about it. It is no big deal anymore… this is the seventies… everything is kosher." She hugged me and turned to go. Her words stayed with me for a while but I dismissed the idea assuring myself that I could turn a new page in my life on my own.

It is only today in looking back that I regret not taking her advice seriously. I believe that had I listened to Deborah and received some help and support I could have dealt much better with my feelings of guilt and shame.

My grief took on many stages and levels of mourning. It was a tremendously difficult time for me, but I never lost touch with that still and solid core deep inside myself. I was able to detach and stand tall even while my head was lowered in sadness. I could feel the force that moved me and had lifted me many times before from the lowest to the highest places. I recognized its still power, its unbreakable strength. Somehow, I knew it was there all along as was my very breath. I finally turned my anger around and used its energy for strength.

First, I needed to clean up what was in front of me. I spent many hours sorting and eliminating things I did not find use for anymore. As I knew I would be leaving this place soon, I searched the newspaper and found a fine apartment close to the Tel Aviv University in Ramat Aviv. It was only a few miles from where Dan and I had lived but its effect was like it was hundreds of miles away. I remembered the Hebrew words, "changing one's place could change one's destiny."

I moved to my new apartment the next Friday evening. My sister and brothers helped in my move and stayed over to keep me company. It did not take too long as I took with me as little as possible. Many of my possessions had lost their attraction and seemed useless. The apartment was small and plain. I had a futon on the floor and many pillows for comfort. Above it I hung a handwoven rug that

Dan had brought home from his trip to Spires. I organized a few red bricks to hold some shelves for my books, and threw down a small area rug my father had brought on his only visit to my home after my wedding. It was a sweet but bitter reminder. Although I cherished his late acknowledgment of me after my wedding, I still had to hide from myself the bitter fact that he abandoned me one more time after Dan's death.

Having my own place felt good but I could not escape the loneliness that I often felt. I was desperate for support and words of encouragement. One evening, months after Dan's death, I called Gideon. With trembling fingers I dialed his number and firmly held the receiver. "Hello, Gideon, this is Sara… do you remember me?" I hoped for a great welcome but held my breath waiting.

"Of course." A loud horselaugh greeted me. I recalled that Dan used to gesture to me to come closer to the receiver and listen to Gideon's horselaugh. It was his trademark or perhaps his way of covering up his feelings. "I am so glad to hear from you. I feel bad for not calling you… How are you? Where do you live now? I am sure everything is under control… no reason to worry about you. You are a girl who has what it takes." He spoke fast and loud as if he was trying to fit in as much as possible in the shortest time.

"I am not so sure of anything anymore, Gideon," I replied carefully opening my heart.

"What do you mean?"

"I am so down…" My voice weakened and interrupted the flow of my words.

"You are down… why?" he asked and burst into laughter. His laughter carried far beyond the receiver. I patiently

waited for his laugh to die down, but even before it reached
its crescendo the next wave came on.

"Gideon... what is so funny?"

"You are funny. Why shouldn't I laugh... are you still
mourning? It is almost a year," he said, laughing again.

"Three months," I quickly corrected him.

"So, three months... I knew that... it seems like a year...
and it is enough. It's finished. Can't you realize that?" He
laughed again. "I think you have to get busy. What are you
doing with your time?" he demanded.

"I am taking art," I said quietly.

"Art? What are you going to do with art? Don't you
need real work?" he asked.

"I will go back to teaching. But not right away... Art
is my passion. I am painting in oil now."

"Sara, you have got to be realistic."

"I am... my painting is a great source of comfort."

"All right... all right, but why are you so down?" he
asked again.

"Oh, I am so sorry and helpless," I sighed.

"Helpless... you helpless?" he laughed. He paused for
a few short moments and then continued. "Are you still
there?" He must have heard me weeping for he added, "Are
you crying?" His voice changed in surprise.

"I'm sorry, Gideon. I shouldn't..." but I could not control my tears, and the more I cried, the quieter he got on
the other end of the line.

"Gideon, do you remember when I first met Dan at
your party? It was a night with so many hopes. I had just
started teaching. I had so many plans for myself, so many
aspirations." I wiped my tears and cleared my thoughts. "I
had this wonderful ambition of teaching the new genera-

tion for greatness… I had so many dreams."

"I remember that night… it was great fun." He joined me for a short moment of reverie but then quickly returned to the present time. "You must stop doing this," he said, and his voice had a sense of anger in it now. "It is not good to go to the past… I have told you… it is done and finished. You can't revive Dan with your memories… you can't bring him back with your cries… it is done and gone… he is dead!"

"But how can you just like that erase it all?" I wondered aloud.

"I can. Just as Dan could remove himself… erase himself from the face of the earth… I can erase him, too." His laughter had finally died out completely and silent fury took its place. I could hear the pain in his heavy breathing and a deep refusal to make peace with Dan. His voice went up and down cracking between his words.

"Gideon, listen. I can't help but feeling guilty sometimes."

"We all feel guilty," he retorted.

I was surprised to hear of his guilt. "Do you miss him?" I asked after a long while.

"I don't know… I don't know." He shared his frustration openly in a quiet and kind voice. "I guess I am angry with him… and I am sorry you have to go through all of this." Slowly, his voice came back to normal. "But, you will be fine. I just know that."

"I wonder sometimes," I said.

"Don't wonder… it is not time to wonder," he replied. His voice was loud and dry as if he was issuing an order. "It is time for you to take charge of your life… How can you be faithful to his memory? Look what he did… not you!

Suicide was his problem, not yours." Gideon's laughter had completely faded by now. For the first time he spoke with earnestness.

"Listen, Sara. I have known Dan since grammar school. We were close friends even then. You knew that, didn't you?" He waited for my answer and I silently nodded my head at my end of the phone. "I know a lot about him. As children we shared what was in our hearts… I know about his mother… and how he felt. I know about his father… a depressed, hard-hearted man! Dan had many issues before you even came along… But he was a great friend. A good man." Gideon stopped for a while as if he wanted to make sure no one was listening. I held the receiver as close as possible to my ear.

"I want you to know that you were a great help in Dan's life… more than you will ever know… so please… get on with your life. Go to sleep now and remember what I have just said," he added quietly in an almost fatherly way.

I put the receiver back in its cradle. I glanced at my black dress and heard Gideon's laughter echoing in the background again. His words still rang in my ears. "Get on with your life." There was a sense of authority in his voice as if he gave me permission to live and expand my future. His words were like an admission ticket to a new world.

The next morning I woke up on the futon in the same position that I had laid down last night. I straightened my dress and all of a sudden the whole idea of wearing black did not make sense to me anymore. Suddenly, I wanted to tear it off and yell with rage, with relief. I got up and took off my dress, rolled it into a ball of cloth and tossed it into the kitchen trash can. Then, I walked into my bedroom and looked at myself in the mirror. I rubbed my eyes, as if wishing to see a new me. My face was still pale and I looked older. Abruptly, I picked up my head. I silently promised myself that nothing would stop me. As long as I lived, I wished to breathe clean air and look into the spring of my life. I smiled and nodded with determination.

Spinning around, I rushed to my closet and swung the doors wide open. My hands dove into the wardrobe and pulled out all my colored outfits. I threw them into the air and danced around as they landed on the bed. Everything was possible now.

The deep force within me was resonating again and I felt myself lifting out of my emotional slumber. I put on a lovely light green dress, drew the lipstick on my lips very gently and brushed back my hair. Once again I glanced at the mirror and nodded with approval. "Viva life!" I called with open laugher.

Outside was a bright sunny morning. The sky was clear and the air fresh. I heard a few birds singing at the edge of my window.

CHAPTER 20

Empowerment

They always say time changes things, but you actually have to change them yourself.
—Andy Warhol

It was early April 1971. Spring had arrived as it did every year. It was a picture-postcard morning, the sun rising and shining through the silver clouds. Trees were dressed up in various shades of green, yellow and sienna. Easy soft breezes caressing the entire scene. Colorful flowers blooming from every corner. Downstairs at the neighborhood flower shop I noticed the many orchids rising up among the other blooms, standing tall with huge open petals. There were hundreds of them in many different colors, but the white ones looked the most wholesome to me.

Spring had arrived regardless of my recurrent gloomy mood and in spite of my personal grief. It had made its way through in all of its splendor. I had always loved this time of the year. It had always been a sign of life in the making.

This particular morning a bluebird had flown into my

room through the wide-open balcony. It started to beat its wings furiously against the opposite window in an effort to fly outside again. I could see she was inhibited and fearful. Rushing to its rescue, I opened the part of the window that was not open, but the bird kept on beating against the closed part of the window and could not see the other side that was open. She was too close to the pane and frenzied in her effort to break free; she could not see anything else. I watched her for a long moment and finally guided her toward the open part of the window where she flew away free.

As I was helping the bird to find her way out to freedom, I came in touch with my own struggle with guilt, shame and self-pity. I, too, seemed to be beating my wings against the closed window of my universe, not realizing that there was an opening right there next to me. It was a good metaphor and a helpful one in the days to come. I walked slowly into my kitchen and got a cup of coffee, looking out on the balcony and wondering about the freed bird while questioning my own constraints.

Finally, I left my apartment and drove along the Mediterranean beach with no purpose or particular destination in mind at all. On my left was the beautiful blue of the sea and on my right side the spread of a city with all its activities. Enjoying the solitude, I rolled the car window open and let the cool wind blow over me. I turned at a bend in the road and drove as close as possible to the shore. The sea lay in front of me like a giant mirror. I felt as if I was falling under the spell of this magnificent creation and my spirit was lifted high. Leaving my car and walking toward the water, I took off my sandals and rolled my pants above my knees. I walked slowly, luxuriating in the wet sand between my toes, and feeling open and free. The sea always seemed to fill me with a sense of empowerment and liberation.

Slowly, I dodged the calm waves, drawing a long zigzag line with my feet in the wet sand, and watching the water erasing it all away. Gradually, my walking became faster and more confident, and with a rising vigor and determination. I started running as if I had a great destination to reach, as if I had something significant to encounter. I kept on running along the shore for a long time. When I finally stopped, I seemed to be still running with joy, my heart racing with a driving force while my mind was calm and clear. My knees sank into the sand and I dropped down spreading myself under the open sky and feeling the caress of the cool air mixed with the warmth of the sun.

As I looked around, I watched a mother following a child running after his kite. An old man playing with his dog. A cluster of birds flying away over the horizon. It was such an open space, such an invitation to unlimited possibilities. It was excellence in the making. A gentle reminder that life is very fragile and delicate, yet powerful enough to embrace the unpredictable. I suddenly knew that I had to move on, that I had to walk away from the past and create a new space for myself. I had to transform to a point where freedom and self-expression were allowed without restriction, without judgment, without critical self-analysis.

I left the beach with steady steps and a secure heart. There was a peace and calm within me. My decision felt right.

I drove straight to my mom's home. My sister was there as well, as she always liked to hang around with my mom. Recently, there was such a feeling of "coming home" in this tiny apartment of my mother's. There was always plenty of food and a sense of welcome. I walked in and they were happy to see me. "I knew you would stop by today," my mom said happily. "I had a dream about you."

"What kind of dream?" I asked, pleased to know I was on her mind.

"Oh, a good one... always a good dream." She laughed easily and offered me lunch while my sister prepared the coffee. "Sit. Where were you?" my mom asked.

"I can't sit... I have to tell you something," I said full of enthusiasm.

Instantly, there was a concerned expression on my mom's face and I rushed to say, "Oh, it is a good thing... wait till you hear everything." I could not sit so I walked into the living room, pulled a cigarette out of my handbag, and then went back to the kitchen to help my mom. I took the plates from her hand and placed them on the dining room table.

"What is it? Are you okay?" my mom finally asked.

"Oh yes, I am. I truly am."

"You seem to be restless. Has something happened?"

"Oh my God, no... nothing happened... I was at the beach."

"Why didn't you tell me? I would have come with you," my sister cried.

"Listen... I want to share something with you, something really great. I just was thinking about everything while walking on the beach... I don't think I belong here anymore... so listen to me." I held onto my sister's hand and pulled her closer to me. I could not control my voice. It came out in a high pitch.

Both my mom and my sister came over very close, eager to hear what it was that I had to say. "What? What?" my sister asked, almost frozen with the empty cup of coffee in her hand.

"Well… let's see…" I played with their curiosity enjoying their interest in my plan and feeling more and more empowered by my decision.

"Well, what?!" she burst out.

"I think I am going to write to the Jewish education office in Los Angeles, New York, London and other big cities in the world… I want to move there."

"Why?" my mom asked with a hint of concern.

"I'd like to see if I can teach abroad. I could teach Hebrew. After all, I am a teacher. They always need teachers… I will go wherever they want me… I shall try them all." I spoke fast, my voice ringing with excitement.

"You're thinking of going away?" My sister looked wary. "Yes, going away to a new place, a new beginning. Just imagine… a totally fresh start for me." I waited for their reaction. They were silent for a long moment, taken aback by my new idea, not sure what to say.

"Leaving, just like that?" my sister repeated with a questioning look on her face.

My mother moved closer to me, straightening her apron with almost a nervous movement. "What would you do there on your own? It is not your country, or your language… it can't be safe," my mom opened up. "You can teach here in Tel Aviv."

"It's going to be all right," I assured both of them.

"It's too risky for you," my mother concluded.

"I will be okay… I have a plan."

She shook her head with clear dissatisfaction. "What will people say?" she said while moving back toward the kitchen.

"I don't really care anymore," I said looking at my sister for approval.

"It sounds like good idea to me," my sister thought out loud and smiled.

"You stop that!" cried my mom, trying to hush my sister and adding with apprehension, "What is the rush? It is not even a year passed since he died. You took off your black dress and now you want to go away?"

"And what is wrong with that?" I interrupted strongly.

"People will talk," she said as she placed the food on the table. "Lets eat something... You should think it over," and she pulled the chair to sit down. "It may look as if you're running away." She kept on talking while nodding her head with worry.

"Running away? What did I do wrong that I need to run away?" I asked firmly. I knew precisely what she had in mind. Even I myself doubted my innocence at times. After all, Dan had told me, "If you leave me, I will kill myself." I could hear him now, his voice echoing in my mother's little apartment. I remember him pleading with me, "Don't leave... don't leave."

For a moment, I disliked myself... I felt truly uncomfortable in my skin. I squirmed in my chair trying to escape my thoughts but feeling overwhelmed with guilt. How many times would I have to deal with this issue of guilt, the ugliest emotion created by human beings? As I resisted it, so it grew deeper. Although I strongly tried to confront and deny its existence, it still seemed to take over and emerge from its hiding place every so often.

"Are you okay?" I heard my sister's voice as if it was coming through a fog.

"Yes. Sure... why are you asking?" I spoke in a suddenly strained voice.

"You are very quiet," she replied.

"I didn't mean to upset you… but you know people talk," my mom hurried to answer and smoothed her hands over her apron. I was puzzled; a mixture of anger and remorse filled my heart. Once again, and I did not know what to do. I glanced at my mother, ready to charge back at her, to tell her off… to throw my anger at her. But I had to forget. I had to move on.

"People will talk," she said again.

"I don't care!" I said after a long pause, staring at her. "I don't care at all. I don't need anyone." I could hear the words coming out of my mouth. I could hear how I was deceiving and isolating myself with my anger. Denying my needs and my longing for closeness and kindness. I was like an agitated puppy feverishly running from one corner to the other, from one person to the other looking for a stroke of acceptance, searching for rest and calm.

"I don't care about what people will say!" I got up ready to leave but before I left, I kept on speaking with assertiveness as if I was shoring up my internal resolve. "My mind is made up. I shall start today… I need to find out the addresses and the names… I need to have a copy of my credentials. And a few letters of recommendation from the school I worked for… I am sure I can get some. Most probably I need to translate them to English with a notary. I will start doing what I have to do right now."

"If you want to get back to teaching, that's good," my mother replied. "There are plenty of schools right here in Israel. Why go so far away from family and your country?" She reached out to me and made a gesture with her hand asking me to sit next to her.

As I looked at her face, I suddenly realized that she and I were so much alike. I appreciated her caring and assured her, "I am not going away for good. Maybe just for a year... one school year. And if it doesn't work out, I will be back here sooner. In fact, I can purchase a round trip ticket good for the entire year."

"Is there such a thing?"

"I'm sure there is. Anyhow I will have a 'plan B' just in case things do not work out." In my sense of security again I sent a kind smile toward her.

"That's the smart thing to do," she said, and handed me a cup of coffee. Once again, I felt a great sense of confidence and self-reliance. An influx of energy and courage took over me and stayed with me over the next few months. I began to re-create myself and proceeded to take action in order to have my plan come to life.

I corresponded with several education offices overseas and eventually chose to focus my attention on the Bureau of Jewish Education in Los Angeles. I received a letter from them saying that they would like to meet me upon my arrival. There were no guarantees in their letter that I would, in fact, have a teaching position, but at least it was an opening and that was good enough for me.

At the same time, I searched the classified ads in the morning and evening newspaper in Tel Aviv with the hope of finding a connection with American people living in Israel. My purpose was to learn more about life in the U.S. and perhaps find some friendships. I met Marsha, an American widow with two kids who came to Israel to turn a new page in her life. I first spoke with her on the phone and found out that she lived not too far from me. We met for coffee.

Our first meeting was very emotional and we instantly connected and understood each other. She was a woman in her late thirties with round hips, a rosy complexion and a continuous smile. She spoke a little Hebrew and asked me repeatedly to correct her when she made a mistake. In return, I practiced my English. It must have been quite funny to see us speaking in two broken languages using our hands to demonstrate our thoughts and opinions. But, I found that over time our limited vocabulary forced us to become more direct and authentic because we did not have the luxury of many words to polish and refine our thoughts. We spoke honestly and at times with boldness.

One day we met for coffee at the corner café. Marsha ordered a cheese croissant, a slice of chocolate cake and a tall milk shake. "You can share it with me," she said.

"Thanks but I will have my Turkish coffee," I said sincerely and pulled out my cigarette.

"Everybody smokes here," she observed.

"You don't smoke?" I asked while taking my first puff.

"No, I don't smoke," she laughed. "I eat!" She pointed to the chocolate cake and cut a big bite with her fork.

"How can you stay so skinny?" she laughed with her mouth full. "The food here is the best." She put her palms together and nodded her head with pleasure to make sure I understood her Hebrew. "But everything is different here… life is different," she said taking a big gulp of her milk shake.

"How long have you been in Tel Aviv?" I asked.

"In August it will be one year. One year is enough for me. It is all I can take." We laughed again. "I have two little boys and they miss their friends in Los Angeles."

"I understand," I said, glad to hear that she was from the same place I already felt linked to. I told her about my plan and my misfortune with my late husband. "He killed himself!" I said it fast but with a sense of tragedy hoping for her compassion.

"I'm sorry... my husband passed away from a heart attack." She placed her palm on her heart. There was a short silence as I wondered what the difference was between the widow of a heart attack victim and the widow of a suicide. I noticed immediately, however, that she did not judge me nor was she uneasy about Dan's suicide. Instead, she went on to share with me about her difficult childhood and her mother's illness. "Since I was a little girl, I remember my mother was always in and out of the hospital," she said sadly.

"I am sorry. What?" I inquired.

"She is sick here." Marsha pointed to her temple. "She is in the crazy people's place." She paused as if to determine my reaction. She, too, had her secrets.

"I am sorry, Marsha." I inhaled deeply from my cigarette. "That must be a harsh way to grow up... to see your Mom... like that." I put my hand on her palm with compassion.

"My father put her there." She spoke as a child would speak with a soft and hesitant voice. "He used to have many girlfriends... it was hard for my mom to see all that... I knew the truth... but I couldn't tell."

I held her hand with sympathy. "And your father... where is he now?"

"Oh, my father lives the good life in California."

"Do you see him?"

"Yes, he helps me... He's rich." She opened her eyes and her hands at the same time.

I laughed. "Rich is good," I said, but Marsha seemed thoughtful.

"You know, my mother almost killed herself, too. But

we don't talk about it… It was bad… I remember my father…" She stopped short and looked uncomfortable. Looking at her wristwatch she told me she had to pick up her boys from school.

"I want to meet with you again, Marsha… Come visit me at my apartment." I grabbed the napkin from our table and wrote down my address.

"Tomorrow?" she asked with a smile.

"Yes, tomorrow," and I smiled back.

We met many times after our first encounter but never again did we mention suicide. It was almost as if we had a silent agreement. But, we did build up a nice companionship. She told me about L.A. with a light in her eyes, and she got excited when she spoke about her home in the Hollywood Hills. For me, it was another piece in the miraculous development of my plan.

When I told her about my purchase of a round trip ticket to L.A., leaving in July, she gave me a big hug and a great smile. She then pulled out of her handbag an envelope and handed it to me. "This is my address in L.A., you will stay with me. I will be there shortly after you arrive and I have a big house." I wrapped my arms around her round body and stayed there for a long moment; I did not let go until I felt her wishing to be released. Finally, I unlocked my arms and made an effort to hide my tears. I was so touched by her offer and a rush of gratitude filled my whole being.

She gently took the envelope from me and pulled the paper out for a quick explanation. "This is Margo's phone number… I already told her about you. Call her when you get there. She's taking care of my house." Marsha pointed her finger to the number at the bottom of her note.

When I got home, I told my mom and everyone who would listen about my friendship with Marsha, my plan to be in L.A. for one year, my correspondence with the Jewish education office and my hopes for a new start.

"You've got to remember that they are not promising anything," Gideon said when I read the letter to him.

"I know, but it is going to be just fine. Look here, I have two recommendations from my school's principal in Tel Aviv and the elementary school in Kiryat Gat where I first worked as a teacher."

"Yes, that should be helpful," he agreed.

"I can always come back. I have a round trip ticket," I reassured him and myself.

I rented my apartment on Sokolov Street to a young couple and asked my brother, Carmel to manage the rent money. The news spread pretty fast among family and friends. Most everyone found my idea to be a good one. In fact, Barak and Debbie looked at me with admiration for my ambition and my courage to try a new place.

"Change is good," Debbie said. "You will be just fine… exploring the new world."

"It will be good for you. Go," Barak said with a big grin on his face, brushing his thick mustache with his fingers, "I will take you to the airport when the time comes."

"Thank you, but it is not until July." Secretly, I welcomed his invitation.

"Two months will pass before you know it," he smiled.

My mother tried to stay out of the way and did not say much after my first talk with her. Aunt Doris looked at me with meaningful expressions on her face when she first heard the news. "No one will know you there… you will be free to do whatever you wish."

Uncle Abraham's reaction was the most interesting. "I am glad you are not leaving to go to England," he said at one of his visits to my mother's home.

"Why?" I inquired.

"Did you know that suicide used to be a felony in England?" He stretched his legs and yawned.

"What do you mean?"

"Well, up until not too long ago, statutes were enacted against those who attempted suicide." He paused, waiting for my reaction.

"But how can they control… someone who wants to kill himself?" I asked.

"True… that's why in 1961, not too long ago, mind you, when the English court discovered that they couldn't prevent people from taking their life, the Parliament enacted a bill removing the criminality of suicide."

"Oh, I can't believe that," I said.

"Believe it… people see suicide as an insult to humanity… plus it's a taboo with many religious traditions. Did you know that Judaism considered suicide a violation of the Ten Commandments?"

"Yes, I know that. But, how do you know all the rest of the information?" I was puzzled.

"I am reading about suicide and how society reacts toward people who kill themselves."

"Interesting," I said flatly, as I could not find a better word.

"Anyway, now for the first time in a thousand years suicide is not considered a felony in England."

Sitting on the sofa next to him, I could not help but ask, "And how about the U.S.?"

"Over there it's always better, and especially now

because in recent years good laws have been established."

"Like what?"

"Two years ago, in 1968, the American Medical Association wrote… and he reeled it off from memory: "'Where a state by statute provides that attempted suicide is a misdemeanor… since no penalty is attached… the misdemeanor of attempted suicide cannot be legally created,'" he smiled, proud of his knowledge. "It's most fascinating to read," he continued. "After all, the laws in the United States were based on English common law, and suicide was believed to be a double curse against both God and the King."

"So what now?" He had gotten me gravely concerned. "Do you still think I should go to America?" I asked sincerely.

"Oh yes! Here they have already condemned you… they got the verdict out long ago," he chuckled aloud. "Suicide is believed to be a part of the physical and psychological makeup of the suicidal person." He put his hand on my shoulder. "You will be okay," and he warmed me with a fatherly smile.

"This all happened only two years ago?" I whispered out loud. I repeated myself louder this time. "Only two years ago?"

"Yup, you just made it," He laughed loudly waiting for me to join him.

I did not find it amusing.

CHAPTER 21

Cookies from Grandma Sophie

The wisest men follow their own direction.
—Euripides (484 BC - 406 BC)

I met Barak at my mother's home. He had arrived early that morning to drive me to the airport where I was to take the direct flight from Tel Aviv to L.A. My brother, Carmel, followed him with his car, an old Ford he had purchased two weeks prior after his release from the army. My mom and her husband, Momo, joined him in the back seat and my sister, Rechel, sat in front next to Carmel. Uncle Abraham stopped by on his way to work to say a final good-bye. He handed me a small bag of cookies.

"This is from Grandma Sophie. She could not stop talking about you last night. She baked these cookies for you."

"I will miss her." I opened the bag of cookies, took one of them out and offered the rest to everyone else.

"Those are for your flight," said Abe and he pushed the cookies away with his palm.

"That's all right… they do serve meals on the plane, you know," Barak interrupted reaching around Abe for a cookie.

"Okay then, but Mom said to tell you this, '*It is good to have a dream.*' She said you would know what she means." Uncle Abraham moved closer to me and shrugged his shoulders with a puzzled expression.

"Is that what she told you?" I smiled to myself and softly tapped my hands on the hardcover folder in my hand.

"What is that?" Uncle Abraham asked curiously.

"Oh, these are some of my drawings… and a book I am writing."

"A book?" He was shocked. "When did you start writing a book?" Uncle Abraham couldn't help asking. "Nobody tells me anything these days." He looked around.

"Right away, after his death," I replied, speaking of Dan as if he was a distant entity.

Barak turned to me and said, "I thought you were not going to tell anyone." He smiled lovingly.

"Well, it's not a secret. Besides, I don't know if I will ever publish it." I looked at both of them waiting for some kind of approval.

"Are you taking this with you? Are you going to write or paint on the plane?" Abe continued his inquiry with a hint of sarcasm.

"Ah yes," I said raising my voice with confidence. "These are the dreams."

"Well, now I understand… you and Grandma…" He made a fast turn away from the car door and then paused to conclude. "Grandma was always ahead of her time… a merchant of fabric, a landlord, a builder... but I don't recall any interest in art... never mind writing," he laughed not waiting for an answer. "I have to go now... take good care of yourself." He took quick steps away avoiding any emotional farewell.

The rest of the family stayed with me to the last minute at the airport. It was quite an emotional and exciting event, but I could not wait to get to L.A. to turn the page in my story, to begin with a fresh start... get familiar with the unknown. I was full of aspiration and had a deep trust in my journey and myself. At the airport, Barak was devoted to helping me. He checked in my suitcase and waited with me at the gate until the plane took off. I could read my mother's concern on her face as she leaned on her husband's arm. My brother kept on reminding me to write and my sister looked at me with a mixture of envy and pride.

"Let us know how you're doing there. You can always use the phone numbers I gave you. Those people owe me a favor." Barak held my hand and reminded me of the people he knew in the states. "In fact, you should call Ezra right away. He works for the Israeli embassy in L.A. and I spoke to him about you last week. He knew Dan pretty well."

"I will," I said with self-assurance.

In L.A., I took the first job that was offered to me... a third grade Hebrew teacher in a Jewish private school in North Hollywood. At first, I stayed with Margo and Marsha but soon I was able to afford my own apartment. I fell in love at first sight with L.A. and for a long time I enjoyed the newness in the air. I especially loved the early morning fogs in June and September, the warm summer nights, the snow on the surrounding mountains. I loved the clean streets, the open spaces, the beautiful homes and the people… totally supporting your wishes and dreams, no matter how far out they might be. The ideas of "whatever makes you happy," or "you can do it if you think you can," were refreshing and empowering. It was the Seventies and I felt right at home.

I used many of my contacts and found people to be most friendly and helpful. I took a few classes at the local Hebrew university to enhance my teaching credentials and to allow me to work and stay in the U.S. legally.

Feeling at home immediately, I behaved like a child who was finally allowed to use the entire playground. I was in touch with a new and uplifting energy and embraced the feeling of being my own self. The university was a good place for me to feel productive and to participate in life. I lifted my head up high. I was content now. At the end of the day I used to roll the windows of my car down allowing the cool air to play in my hair and letting the self-approval grow deeper. I corresponded with my family and friends and visited Israel every summer at the school break, and every summer I decided to extend my stay in L.A. for another year. The first seven years I went back and forth, not sure where my permanent residence should be. I never sold the apartment at Sokolov St. in Tel Aviv and it became my link to Israel and my family's hope that one day I would be back for good.

My brother, Carmel, kept on reminding me that Israel was my homeland and I should not abandon it. My Grandma Sophie never forgot to ask, "Are you still painting, and how about the book?" Uncle Abraham always interrupted with the thought that he was not worried so much about my artwork and the book as my finding a good husband for myself.

One day I wrote him back:

> Dear Uncle Abraham,
> I think you will be pleased to know that I am painting now in oil and acrylic and taking sculpting classes once a week. I love my life in L.A. I am also continuing to work on my book as I think it is worthwhile to tell my story.

I vividly recall his reply. It was a quick response and it was very short and clear:

> Maybe the book is not such a great idea. Try not to think too much about Dan and Dan's death. You have to put it behind you as soon as you can.

That was our last correspondence regarding my book. I made an attempt to publish my story, but received letters of rejection from a few publishers claiming that the story was not marketable enough. I realized it was too painful for me to rewrite it and make it suitable for Hollywood. Therefore, I thought to myself that maybe Uncle Abraham was right. After all, what was the use of going back and rehashing old wounds? So, eventually, I excused myself from writing and stashed the manuscript among other forgotten and unneeded items. But I made sure it was well protected as it felt like it was a vital part of me.

I kept on teaching and enjoying what was in front of me. I kept on looking for love and fulfillment in the creative process of art and in my connection with men.

I met Steve at one of the early education classes. We connected right away, and became fully occupied with each other, in spite of the age gap between us. Steve was only nineteen years old while I was twenty-five and already considered a woman with a past. I enjoyed the instant gratification of the moment and did not think too much about anything else as long as he seemed happy to have me in his arms. To me, it was the pleasure of being able to move along feeling free without the fear of 'what will people say?' I loved the affection and felt drunk under the influence of the great big world of Hollywood and the magical Beverly Hills.

Steve was energetic, attractive and fun to be with. I felt freer than I ever had before. We toured the city and took trips to Las Vegas and other sights on the spur of the moment. I loved his Mustang convertible and was proud to lean on his strong muscular arm. Once again, I was creating my own fantasy and felt as if I was emerging out of a glamorous movie script. Together we watched some of the huge 1970's marches for women's liberation, listened to the chanting of Hare-Krishnas and enjoyed the lyrics of freedom songs.

One day we came to the streets of Westwood, which were filled with men and women observing the colorful chanting and marching. I could not help but notice a radio reporter who moved among the crowd interviewing people. He was tall and stood up above the others. His voice was deep with a ring of authority. His smile was certain and he moved among the crowd gracefully. I followed him with my eyes as closely as I could. Our glances met a few times and I moved my body closer hoping he would approach me.

As I got within a few feet from him, I noticed that he was fair with more than a few freckles covering his forehead. I stared at his thick, long hair framing his face. The sun picked up shades of red, and I fantasized putting my fingers through it. I watched him putting his microphone away and walking toward me. I took a deep breath and suddenly wished I were there by myself.

"Hi," he said. "My name's Sean. What do you think about all this?" he asked both of us pointing at the crowd.

"I think spirituality is a great concept and women ought to be free... it will be good for us, man," Steve rushed to answer with a sense of importance. But Sean kept on staring at me. I was drawn to him like a magnet.

"So what do you think?" He specifically nodded at me.

"I think we shouldn't have to fight for it... we should just take it."

"Take what?" Sean laughed.

"Our freedom," I answered. "After all, no one can take it away from you unless you give it to them." I thought I sounded very clever.

"And where are you from?" he asked, probably noticing my heavy accent.

"I'm from Israel," I replied proudly.

"Ah... I understand... women get drafted in Israel, don't they? Did you go into the Army?" He motioned for us to move away from the crowd.

"No, I did not," I said.

"Why not?" he asked with surprise.

"I got married instead," I explained. "I had just turned eighteen when I got married... they do not draft wives." We laughed. Sean looked at Steve.

"And, are you her husband?"

Steve shook his head no and I thought I saw a look of relief flicker across Sean's face. I rushed to say that we were just friends.

"Well, you sound extremely intelligent... it seems to me you will have interesting opinions about women's liberation and everything else," he said while pointing at the Hare-Krishna group.

I nodded discreetly as I wished to have an opening, a reason to see him again.

"As I said, my name's Sean and I'm from KBLA radio station." He extended his hand to me, then to Steve. We smiled and exchanged our names. "I'd like to give you my card... maybe we could meet and talk."

Inside I was delighted but outside I tried to keep a straight face. I could feel my heart fluttering as his thick lips moved under his unshaved short whiskers. He handed me his card and we turned to leave but not before Steve wrapped his arms around me as if to demonstrate our intimate connection.

"He likes you," Steve said thoughtfully as we walked away. "I can't leave you alone for a second and even when I am around..." Steve did not finish his sentence leaving the silence to me.

"He is cute... don't you think?" I said playfully and drew him closer.

"An Irish guy," Steve stated. "Are you going to call him?" he asked with concern.

"How do you know that he is an Irish guy?" I laughed, interested in any extra insights.

"I just know, but are you going to call him?"

I chose not to answer. Instead I pulled Steve by the hand and skipped over to the other side of the street. "Where are you going?" he laughed behind me.

"Anywhere..." I was happy and full of joy thinking about Sean. I felt like a young teenager and wondered if what had just happened with him was "love at first sight?" Everything had suddenly become meaningless. Everything but my thoughts of Sean.

People were leaving the area but some Hare-Krishna disciples were still playing their drums, wearing orange and chanting for peace and love. How appropriate all that felt for me. Peace and love. The great concept of "make love not war" of the Seventies was a perfect match with me. I absorbed it immediately and wanted more. It could not have happened at a better time. I felt ripe to search for the meaning of life, to soothe my soul with spirituality and the understanding of life's shaking and trembling. To be able to live this moment as totally as possible because the next moment might not come, ever. It was a great concept and I did everything to ride with it, but it was not easy to do so with Steve at my side.

I waited a few long days to call Sean as I did not want to appear too eager. When I called, I was pleased to learn that he remembered my name immediately and was happy to hear from me. He told me that he was leaving on a business trip the next day. "I wish you had called earlier," he said, and asked for my phone number promising to call me upon his return. Of course, I was disappointed and wondered if our conversation was a polite way of rejection.

I kept my relationship with Steve casual. I suddenly realized that I could chat with him easily about a thousand and one nonsensical things but that we rarely talked seriously. One night he asked me, "How did your husband die?"

There was an awkward gap of silence. Something in me held back the truth and I replied without the blink of an eye, "He was a casualty of comeback operations." I looked directly into Steve's eyes hoping he would end his questioning.

"Where? In Lebanon?" he helped me.

"Yes," I answered, immediately feeling uncomfortable and wishing to change the subject.

"I'm sorry... how did it happen?" he continued.

"I'd rather not talk about it," and I stopped him cold. I did not think too much about it at that moment but one lie forced me to create the second and the third. I did not like the feeling in my body: the sinking sensation of a covert, the fear of being revealed and the need to guard every word from then on. But for now, lying was less painful than confronting the truth. Lying did not keep the past away, in fact, the hesitation, the vagueness and the cloudiness kept on and it felt like sometimes it was my imprisonment.

I realized that it had nothing to do with Steve as he was enjoying our interaction and not looking to talk about each other's troubles. But it had everything to do with me and my concern about being judged and blamed. It was much easier to talk with Steve about the women's liberation movement, Jewish education and other intellectual topics. I had no intention at all of opening my heart to him, especially since I had heard him talking about people with a sense of superiority.

"So why aren't you marching for women's liberation?" Steve asked me a couple of days after meeting Sean. "You would fit in right away."

"I am already liberated," I charged back. "I liberated myself... and I don't need anyone's permission to do so." I was proud in my ignorance and defended my position with vigor.

"I love your strength," he said. "I love your self-assurance." While embracing himself with those thoughts, he started planning and speaking about our future together. "I want to spend the rest of my life with you," he declared, even as I was just starting to reclaim my lost years and rebelling against anything that would tie me down.

So, just to make sure that no one had an exclusive ownership of me and that I could always fill up my need for love, I got together with Ezra, Barak's old friend, the next day.

"You are beautiful and smart," Ezra said even before I spoke. I smiled and my heart was filled with strength. Did he say smart? That alone could earn him a lot of credit with me. I immediately placed my trust in him.

"I did hear that Dan had a beautiful wife… but it is not until now…" he held my hand in his right palm and caressed it meaningfully looking at me through his glasses with a most desirable smile. I was taken in by his compliments and absolutely infatuated with the pedestal he had just placed me on. It reminded me of Dan. "I also want you to know that I don't think that Dan's death is any reflection on you… and I don't care what anyone says. You know this is a small world… people talk… but not me." His lack of authenticity was undeniable.

Ezra, a stocky, short man in his forties, pale faced and tense had very little to be desired but I overlooked that. I noticed that at first my body did not respond positively to his remarks. I was ready to accept his words, no questions asked. I ignored the unsettled feeling in my stomach, the numbness in my throat, the sudden lack of words. It had happened to me before where I became frozen and couldn't resist and it was happening again. I felt stunned by the fact that I was in L.A. now and I still had to deal with people talking.

My only and immediate concern was to please others with the hope of being appreciated and accepted. All I heard and believed was Ezra's smooth and sweet talk. However, the protest of my body remained strong, and I believed I heard Dan's voice echoing in the background repeating one more time, "You are so naive, my dear." Naive? I always felt that naive was only a sweeter word, a kinder expression for being stupid.

Ezra kept on staring at me waiting for me to say something. "Would you join me for dinner tonight? I would be most grateful to be seen in your company." He slanted his head in a childlike way with a question mark on his face. "Please," he squeezed my hand. "You are so special, so beautiful."

I nodded my head and smiled back while abandoning myself to the sugary but empty words that Ezra spoke. It is only in looking back that I can detach myself from the person I was. It is only now with the distance of time and some awareness that I can see my total need and enormous yearning for acceptance. I would offer my soul for just a few crumbs hoping to fill up the hole inside me.

"I will pick you up at seven o'clock," he said and got up to go.

That evening he showed me all the ins and outs of the big city. He seemed to me larger than life and every event was significant. Suddenly, I felt frightened to lose it all. "It is the Seventies, my dear," he said, when I hesitated to check in with him at the hotel that night. "This is a free world. You do what your heart desires. No one here will judge you," he said, as I walked behind him into the room.

But I was not entirely sure what it was that my heart desired. In fact, for the most part, my heart was not there at all. I wonder now, how could I have recognized what was right and what was wrong. I had no measuring stick to go by. I didn't see Ezra any more after that night.

The next morning my mind felt heavier than ever before. I was angry for not being able to take care of myself. My body was furious for being used. I realized that I was still having trouble acknowledging that I had choices. Growth was difficult. It hurt because something within me had to be destroyed and dropped. Only then was the new a possibility.

In my mind the most significant event took place a few days later when Sean called and asked me to join him for dinner. In fact, the thought that I was going to be with Sean alone was so exciting that nothing else really mattered. I still felt so dependent on a man to confirm my identity and my reason for being.

I spent hours planning what to wear, washing and setting my hair. First, I pulled it up. Then I tried to braid it but, in the end, I decided to wear my hair with a French twist. I refrained from talking about my date with Sean and did not want to share it with anyone. I just didn't want to jinx it. But, I did tell Marsha that I didn't ever recall feeling like this before. I admitted to her that I was experiencing that famous condition of "butterflies in the stomach." The idea of sitting at the dinner table alone with Sean seemed enchanting although I was wondering if I would be able to eat at all. I was so nervous.

He rang my doorbell at seven p.m. sharp just as he had said. I was ready and opened the door with eagerness. Sean stood tall at the door holding in his hands a large bouquet of flowers. White orchids! He extended them to me with a big smile. For a moment I felt confused. I looked at him, then at the flowers, then at him again. "Don't you like flowers?" he asked.

"I love flowers... they are beautiful," I stammered and tried to pull myself back to the present time. I invited him in and left the flowers in the kitchen sink.

Our eyes immediately sought each other out and our feelings seemed to be mutual. He was well dressed, the way one dresses up to impress. He asked if I was ready and we left immediately. At the restaurant, Sean held my hand across the table and asked the waitress to bring a bottle of wine. We did not speak about women's liberation or Hare-Krishna. In fact, we didn't speak much at all. We didn't seem to be concerned about anything other than each other. To me, it was absolutely a new phenomenon.

He tested the wine and nodded his head with approval. "You will like this one," he told me while the waiter poured the wine in crystal glasses. We kept on gazing at each other raising our glasses through the evening.

I could not help recalling my conversation with my girlfriend, Shoshana, after her honeymoon when she wondered why people made such a big to-do about sex. "After all, it takes only a few minutes for it to be over," she had said. Sean proved her wrong over and over again and, as for myself, I finally tasted the power of making love! The opening of a tender heart, the full acceptance, the quality of laughter. Like a flower coming from within and blooming on the outside. No need to fulfill anyone's expectations. The only desire in play between Sean and myself was to release ourselves. Unrepressed. Opening and flowing with each other.

When we made love, our entire being was throbbing with it. It became like a meditation. Every part of our body came to life, our breathing deepened and our inner core took on a passionate life of its own. Our bodies met with such an orgasmic energy that the ego disappeared and the whole universe melted and became one. For the first time, all of society's opinion was gone! My love for Sean was like a dance, sometimes wild and sometimes gentle and soft. I was thirsty for him and he quenched my thirst unconditionally.

We spent many nights and days together and, when we were apart, I could not stop thinking about him. I was in love and I felt the ultimate value of joy. All my fears had disappeared and I believed that I was finally free of Dan's ghost... But that was not to be.

CHAPTER 22

My Truth

The truth that makes men free is for the most part the truth
which men prefer not to hear.
—Harbert Agar

Steve kept in touch with me all along, refusing to go away. "How can you do this to me? I know you are seeing Sean," he said. "We had a good time together, didn't we?"

I nodded yes.

"You know I love you... Why are you doing this to me... how can you?"

I did not have a good answer for him. Nor did I care to find one. In fact, I felt indifferent and didn't understand why he just didn't get it. Anything I said only proved that I was insensitive and selfish. All I wanted was to close the page with Steve, no questions asked. No doubt it was egotistical and inconsiderate on my part, but I was so wrapped up in the feelings I was experiencing with Sean that nothing else seemed to matter.

One day, Steve stopped by my apartment uninvited. "I just had to see you," he said when I opened the door. He appeared nervous holding onto the doorframe. I was both surprised and annoyed, wishing that he would just disappear.

"Can I come in?" he asked pushing his body through the door and not waiting for my answer. He walked straight to the refrigerator. "I need something cold to drink," he said, pulling out a can of soda and sitting on the stool in my kitchen.

"So how are you?" he asked, looking for some kind of an opening.

"I'm okay."

"Good," he continued. "I ran into your friend, Marsha, this morning." He paused looking at me as if he was holding me responsible for something.

"I know. She left me a message to call her back… I just got home."

"You should," he said raising his voice. "You should call her back."

"Why? What happened?"

"We talked." He paused again and I felt as if he was angry and deeply hurt yet I had no clue as to why.

"You lied to me," he finally said. "I guess you felt you had to lie to me."

"What about?"

"About your late husband. Do you still want to tell me that he died in an army action?"

I was silent. Not sure what to say. Oddly enough, I believed I owed Steve an explanation but the child in me was scared. I was caught, exposed and Steve was having no mercy at all. This was a profound tool for him to use, a weapon against me to satisfy his rage for me choosing Sean over him. "True. I lied," I finally said. "I'm sorry."

"Why did you lie? Did you have something to do with his death?"

"I don't know," I said, and slowly sat down. It had been so hard for me to tell him the truth when he had first asked. I didn't want to see that look in his face that I saw so often when I told people my husband was a suicide.

He took a big sip from his soda can and breathed easier now. It seemed that his anger was defused somewhat.

"In fact, I am not totally sure about anything anymore," I said as if I was speaking to myself.

Looking within, I knew that I had been thrown into a life with Dan, impressed and infatuated by him, fully preoccupied with the image he portrayed. I believed in the fantasy I had built around him.

However, Dan had been a complicated, wounded man, leading a double life. One expression had been the image he presented to the outside world, and the other was the private, secretive, injured side of himself that not even he could control.

Perhaps the only reason Dan had loved and married me was to sooth his injury, to mold and shape me to fit his needs and wants so he would not have to feel that pain again. He was a man who cried for help but no one could hear him. He was a man who desperately wanted to be understood, and yet, I hardly could understand myself. He was a man who always desired to do the right thing but ended up performing the most fatal and destructive act of all.

Was it my destiny to be part of his pain and destruction? Or, perhaps, it was my own selfish need to be loved and accepted by someone no matter what, to be sheltered from my own fear of abandonment. Believing that Dan's love for me was so powerful, so profound, I thought I would never be left by him, never be deserted again. I couldn't help but recall the famous saying, "Man plans and God laughs."

Oh, the irony of life… the paradox of fate… Dan's act of self-inflicted death was the ultimate abandonment. What a strange weaving our life's fabric had created for each of us. Broken families had instilled a deep-rooted hurt and each of us had gathered and built ideas and desires that sprang from the depths of this childhood. Yet we each took a completely diverse way in our approach and attitude toward life. We ended up going our separate ways but, oddly enough, we stayed connected to our mutual thread of life and death. Even as Dan moved on, I remained to deal with his life's wounds. It was as if he had transferred his injury into my universe.

"Yes, I lied to you, Steve," I whispered after a long silence. "I lied because I don't like my reality. I created a new one for you, for people like you… because dying in the army is acceptable and honored… but dying by suicide is condemned."

"How can you even compare the two?" he agreed.

"Why not… dying is dying… Why do you care how one dies?" I lashed out defensively.

"Of course I care… God cares. Suicide is against life."

"And who are you to know what God cares for?"

"It's not only me thinking so… but the entire society, the scriptures… ask anyone you want," he retorted.

"They all were wrong before," I whined. Suddenly, I stopped myself. *I cannot become Dan's advocate now*, I thought. I struggled to explain his incomprehensible act of self-murder yet no one could help me understand his act. Nothing could bring *me* complete peace and acceptance. I was aware of a mixed feeling of rage and love for Dan. Suddenly, I wished he were here to straighten up this mess I was creating in my life. Moving from Steve to Ezra then to Steve again and finally into the loving hands of Sean.

Not able to rest.

Not able to trust.

I wanted to be alone and asked Steve to leave. "I am tired," I said "I really don't know why anyone would kill themselves."

"Life becomes too hard to handle, I guess," he answered quickly, as if he had it prepared.

"I guess," I agreed.

"So what was it that was so hard for him to handle?" he insisted.

"I don't know," I raised my voice impassionedly.

"Maybe it was you!" he stated. "Maybe it was you, angel face."

If I was to blame, I thought, *then here is my penalty*. No one really needed to assist me in this punishment. I myself was the harshest judge. This was who I had become: the woman whose husband killed himself. The more I tried to deny its presence, the stronger it became.

Life after suicide was simply that: life after suicide.

It shook my foundation; it trembled to the very core of my being. In spite of the fact that most of the time I put on a cheery front, suicide lay inside my being like a sleeping giant, easy to awaken. Here in L.A. things seemed to be no different. Geographically, it was far away. It was a bigger, richer country. It was easier to get lost in a crowd. But here, too, people talked. Here, too, people judged.

Steve stood up still waiting for an answer. "So you did have something to do with his death, didn't you?" he came back vigorously. "No wonder the poor guy killed himself."

"You are crazy... why would you even say such a thing?" I cried.

"Because, it is hard to love you. It is painful to love you. You don't care how I feel... you are seeing Sean and you think it is okay." He stood up ready to leave. "You don't have a heart. You think it is easy to be dumped?" he yelled agitatedly. He moved across the room crushing the soda can in his hand. "I hope one day you experience this pain... one day you will!" He pointed his finger at me with self-assurance.

"I am sorry. I didn't mean to hurt you. What do you want me to do?" I asked frightened by his anger.

"Stop seeing Sean," he demanded.

"I can't," I said and pulled back from him.

"Why can't you? I love you... I want to marry you," and he grabbed my hand.

"I don't want to get married... I don't ever want to get married again." I pulled my hand away raising my voice with shaky determination.

"Of course not. You still want to play." He shrugged his shoulders. "You have a heart of stone." Clearly angry with me, he walked toward the door and pulled it open. He stopped for a moment and faced me. Our eyes met and I could see the disgusted ugly expression on his face. That's what he felt for me now, and I could not escape it. Our kindness for each other had vanished. Love and hate linked so closely to each other.

"I will tell you one thing!" he paused. "I am not going to kill myself!" he said slowly, pointing to his chest. He slammed the door closed behind him.

I remained alone watching my past merge into my present one more time. The fear of Steve's anger was real for me. At first it was hard for me to digest what he had said, but then I was overcome with the thought that he might, contrary to what he said, actually harm himself. I called his home many times that evening, but every time the answering machine picked up, my worry and my fear grew stronger.

I finally called Marsha. "I am sorry," she said. "I really thought he knew about the suicide."

"I understand," I said, "but now I am afraid he will do something stupid."

"I don't think so," she replied with a laugh. "You are not that powerful! My God, people don't kill themselves because of someone else." She sounded so confident. She paused, giving me enough time to absorb what she had just said.

I breathed a sigh of relief. Her logic was healthy and real. It was as if she carried me into a different realm and for a short while I was released from my panic.

"Yes, but I can't reach him. He should be home by now." I waited for her comforting and reassuring words.

"He will be home. You should go to sleep now."

"Really? You don't think he will hurt himself?"

Even after Marsha and I hung up, I couldn't go to sleep. I stayed up that night until it was late. I was trapped in my own fearful thoughts. They narrowed my ability to see. I curled up in my armchair and placed the phone on my lap. Then I kept on calling until he finally picked up the phone. It was sometime after midnight and I was relieved to hear his voice on the other end.

"Are you okay?" I asked.

"Yes, I'm okay. Why would you care?"

"I just needed to know."

The next morning I awoke and began to sort through my feelings of guilt and anger and confusion. With an almost involuntary movement I delved into my creative work as it had always been my outlet. With my hands I could communicate what was even hidden from my own consciousness. I unloaded two bags of clay on my turntable, pulled up my sleeves and looked at it from many different angles. I knew there were possibilities that were hidden in this medium that lay in front of me. Feeling conflicted, I threw myself into my work.

In the next few weeks, I created three images of women with different expressions yet bonded and merging together. I named the piece "One Woman." The desire to be one with every manifestation and every experience of life was clear; to embrace and hold all faces of life free of censure, free of judgment was my wish for every woman. The ending of my work always shed light on my lingering darkness and it forced me to see, to love the process, and to treasure the results. It felt like life could be good again after all.

Later when Sean saw my work he stared for a long moment and finally said, "It is beautiful." He slanted his head looking at the piece from the side. "You keep creating these women. I notice that everything you paint or sculpt has to do with a woman's image... what are you saying?" he asked tenderly.

"I am recreating myself," I laughed. "I don't really know," I corrected myself immediately, feeling humble in the face of my work.

"It is beautiful... but not as beautiful as you are," he said.

"My work is who I am."

"You are my Sara," he murmured back and pulled me close to him. Once more I surrendered in his arms. I used to think that this kind of love never died. It had a fragrance of eternity that put me at ease and allowed me to feel the most vulnerable of feelings. There was no demand from either one of us yet each opened the other. We met at least four evenings a week and spent the nights together, laughing, talking, and loving. In the morning he would bring me home and from there I would take my car to work.

Unlike Steve, he was not interested in my past nor did he ask too many questions. It was an evening more than a year later that we went to a movie theater and watched something that had to do with the Bermuda triangle. Sean said on the way out of the theater, "I grew up in Bermuda."

"Not Ireland?" I asked.

"I was born in Ireland, then my family immigrated to New York when I was three. Finally, we moved to Bermuda." As we entered his apartment, he dimmed the light, lit the big candle on his coffee table with his lighter and kept on reminiscing. "I loved the time in Bermuda. The blue ocean, the beautiful girls and the warm sun." He readjusted the large ashtray as he had many times before and pulled out a small wooden box from the shelf under the coffee table. He placed it on the edge of the table close to his seat.

"It sounds like L.A.," I said.

He laughed. "Not quite... I was younger and carefree."

"Do you miss it?" I asked with envy.

"No, not at all." He turned the music on. "I don't miss anything now... as long as I have you." Sean had a way with words and I did not question them. His words were soothing and complementary, just what I wanted and needed to hear. "And how about you?" he asked.

"Me? Oh, I don't miss the beautiful girls at all."

He laughed easily and opened his wooden box with special care, as a child would play with his new toy. He took out a tiny pipe and emptied it into the ashtray, cleaning it with a small pick. Sean hovered over his possessions with a sense of pleasure and prepared the pipe to be lit. He inhaled deeply, looked at me from the corner of his eyes and offered me the pipe as he always did. I shook my head no and reached for my cigarette.

"When are you going to try it?" I followed him with my eyes as he walked into the kitchen coming back with a bottle of wine and two glasses. "You should try it; grass is nature's way to say 'Enjoy!'"

"One day," I said, still afraid of the unknown.

"I guess you don't need it," he replied pouring the wine into the glasses. "You get that natural high on life... an import from the holy land." We laughed. He sat next to me, still engaged with his pipe and spoke softly. "I suppose you don't have any worries..." He paused and waited for my reaction as I watched the outline of his face in the dim light.

"I don't have such immunity," I said and kissed him lightly.

"Okay, no rush." He took another puff from his pipe and leaned back. He seemed to be totally content within himself.

"I know," I said. Feeling at ease, I took the pipe out of his hand and inhaled. He turned toward me and followed my smoke, making a sign with his hand to keep the smoke in. He held his breath in with me till I coughed the smoke out and reached for my drink.

"How do you feel?" Sean asked after few moments.

"I was born in Baghdad," I said out of nowhere.

"Not Israel?" he laughed.

"My family immigrated to Israel from Baghdad when I was three." I believe I sounded somewhat serious because he looked at me and took another hit from his pipe.

"Baghdad? As of... Ali Baba and his forty thieves?"

He offered me the pipe again. When I nodded yes, we both burst into laughter.

"An interesting story... Please tell me more." He stretched his body on the sofa and laid his head on my lap. I brushed his hair with my hand pulling it away from his forehead.

"Then I moved to L.A.," I said.

"Aren't you skipping anything?" he asked, raising his eyebrows.

"Only twenty-three years," I laughed stroking his chest.

"Why L.A.?" he asked.

"Oh, the blue ocean, beautiful girls and the warm sun," I said flippantly wishing to avoid his question with a smart remark.

"No, really why L.A.?" he asked, and then told me about himself. "I moved to L.A. because I got an offer I couldn't refuse... Reporting from L.A. is a healthy boost for my career."

"Well, I'm glad you did." I felt so relaxed with Sean and was enjoying the state I was in, easy, non-confined, and gladly abandoning the mind. Love is one of those things that is bigger than the mind; it does not happen in the logical world. It needs some degree of surrender. There was a long silence. I knew it was only right for me to share with him my side of the story.

"I guess…" I paused. "I guess… I moved to L.A. after my husband killed himself," I said with a voice that had nothing to hide.

I felt Sean's head moving on my lap. He reached for my hand and kissed it lovingly. "I am sorry," he said. "I am sorry you had to go through such a trauma." He was sincere, squeezing my hand and I wrapped my arm around his chest holding on to it. "I love you," I heard him saying.

I was filled with inner bliss quietly enjoying this sweet taste of his acceptance. I could feel my body release its hesitancy. Sean had left the door to his heart open and I had allowed myself in. Oh, it felt so sweet. Our bodies moved slowly together and we softened into each other's arms. Our lips clung to each other for a long moment. The delightful flavor of affection… the beautiful feeling of losing control in the arms of a lover. It was like being possessed by some unknown force with nothing but our own depth to stop us. It felt so very simple and innocent, the true celebration of who we were as people.

CHAPTER 23

In His Shoes

When you start painting, it is somewhat outside you. At the
conclusion you seem to move inside the painting.
—Fernando Botero

Sean's unconditional acceptance of my past, as well as
him not imposing expectations nor changing his view of
me once he learned of my past, gave me a good reason to
remove all obstacles between us. It elevated my sense of
trust that pure and simple love was, in fact, very possible. I
felt on top of the world and this felt like the most desirable
place to heal my spirit.

Time went by and Sean's presence permeated my being.
I could not stop thinking about him. I placed him on a
pedestal higher than anyone could touch and the longer I
stayed with him, the more my heart depended on him. In
essence, I adored him beyond good or bad, right or wrong,
ugly or beautiful. He was my world. In my mind's eye he
was the perfect man. For me, it was a true, innocent love,
and although I didn't realize it at the time, true love could

be more dangerous than I was willing to admit. It undressed my soul and opened up my entire being as if we were both sharing the same breath.

Sean enjoyed my devotion to him and yet, at times, I felt he was still a little guarded with me. I pushed that nagging feeling away and focused instead on my own feelings for him. In the name of love he assumed all the power and I gave it away. He allowed me to have tremendous freedom to act, to think and to feel, and I was swept away with this acceptance.

"You don't have to change your life just because you're in love," he said to me one day. "Love is like a bird... it is free... you are an artist... you understand the need for your soul to remain free."

My infatuation swallowed up any concerns I might have had and allowed me to hear only what I wanted to hear. "You know, you need to land on earth sooner or later," my friend Marsha said to me shortly after, when I was sharing Sean's comment with her. "You have known him for a little less than two years now and you still don't really know that much about him. You know that he works for the radio, that he is very accepting of you and that you are madly in love with him, but beyond that you don't know much about his past. He hasn't made a commitment to you in terms of marriage or anything solid and yet you have given up your soul to him. I worry about you, that's all. I don't want to see you get hurt."

"My God, Marsha, you sound like my mother." I laughed dismissing her concerns.

"I'm just fearful that maybe this obsession is a little too one-sided."

"Don't be silly, Marsha. He loves me. He has told me

that over and over again. We couldn't make love the way we do if he wasn't in love with me."

"If you're both so in love, then why don't you get married?"

"Do you think marriage is the right answer for everyone?" I retorted. "Who wants to get married?"

"I do," she said staring at me. "If I ever loved someone as much as you love Sean, I would want to marry him."

"Marriage is an unnecessary act... It only complicates people's minds," I insisted basing my belief on my past experience with Dan.

"Well, I just hope you will live happily ever after, married or not," she exclaimed.

"I will," I replied adamantly.

It was not too long after this conversation with Marsha that I was to be proved dead wrong. The incident has stayed vivid in my mind for a long time—the pain and embarrassment still ring loud and clear.

It was on an easy, warm summer evening when Sean called and said he would not be able to see me that night as he needed to stay at the radio station for unexpected work. "Don't wait for me... I'll call you as soon as I can get away," he said.

"That's fine," I replied with no hesitation. "I'll go with Marsha to the movies. She wants to see *The Way We Were* with Barbara Streisand."

"But we've seen it already," he said surprised.

"Yes, but I can see it again with Marsha," I laughed.

"Yes, you can," he agreed. "Just know that I'll be missing you... Be good," he said and ended the conversation quickly.

Marsha picked me up at 7:30 p.m., but she wanted to

stop by her office first to pick up a paper she needed to deliver to a client first thing in the morning. By the time we worked our way through traffic and retrieved the paper, it was too late for the movie so we decided to have a late dinner at the Santa Monica pier instead. We stopped in front of a local seafood restaurant and parked the car. "This is Sean's favorite restaurant," I remarked as we started to walk inside. "I know the menu here almost by heart."

"Enough about Sean... it is girl's night out," she protested while we waited for the host to seat us.

I stood behind Marsha searching in my handbag for a cigarette when suddenly Marsha faced me, clenched her hands on my shoulders, and with an ashen face declared, "Don't look up!"

"What? What's wrong?" I tried to release myself from her grip but she held tight.

"It's Sean," and she pointed to the far end booth almost breathlessly. "Oh my God, Sean is here. You shouldn't look," she murmured.

"Why?" and I finally moved away from her.

"Because he is with a girl," she said and opened her eyes wide.

"With a girl?" I repeated and pushed her gently aside, hoping to prove her wrong. But there he was, leaning over a girl, closely embracing her: their lips touching, their arms caressing. I remained frozen and did not move for a long while. For me, time stopped. I saw Marsha talking with the host and asking to be taken off the list. I saw her looking at me and then back at Sean's table.

"Let's go," she whispered wrapping her arm around me. A cold sweat covered my face and I continued to look over her shoulders. It was Sean. There was no doubt. I recognized the shirt he was wearing; I had bought it for him last Christmas. I was almost able to smell his favorite after-shave and hear the words he had whispered in my ear the last time he wore it. Was he whispering those same words to her now? Was she feeling the same sensation under her skin as he touched her? Her dreamy eyes revealed it all.

I felt at a loss. A sharp pain of jealousy surged in my chest as I surrendered to Marsha and allowed her to guide me out of the restaurant. Once outside in the parking lot, I took a deep breath and looked up at the clear sky. I disengaged from Marsha's caring arms and stood quietly on my own. I turned back and faced the entrance of the restaurant. "I will be right back," I told Marsha and walked inside with steady steps. I knew she followed me as I could feel her concern and caring behind me.

I walked past the host straight toward Sean's table. I stood there in silence a moment. The same bottle of wine we used to order was half empty. The food on their plates was practically untouched. It took them a few short moments to notice me. I stood still, looking directly into Sean's eyes as he lifted his face and slowly disengaged himself from the girl. She looked at me surprised but I believe she had no difficulty interpreting the look on my face. "So, now I understand… love is like a bird," I said with a choked voice, switching my gaze from Sean to the girl and back to Sean again.

"I am sorry," he said while sliding his long body out of his seat. Apologetically, he put his arm on my shoulder. "I can explain… really," he said.

"You don't have to…" I threw his arm aside and left as fast as I could. He took a few steps toward me trying to stop me… but then he allowed me to leave.

On our way back to her apartment, I remained silent

and let Marsha do the talking. "I can explain... I can explain... The son of a bitch can't explain... What the hell is he going to tell you? Are you going to let him explain?" She looked at me waiting for a reply. I shrugged my shoulders with pain, not able to speak. "Men are the mistake of God's creation!" she continued in a blistering voice. "That's okay. Everyone makes mistakes, even God! Men... the sons of bitches!" She was driving fast and stopping at the red lights with a sharp, abrupt halt. I heard her speaking on my behalf with rage, experiencing the anger I could not yet feel. "I hate him... How could he do that? I never trusted the son of a bitch... I was afraid of this all along. There was something I didn't trust about him... his player smoothness, something." She rambled on and the words washed over me.

When we arrived at her apartment, she opened the door sharply and walked straight to the refrigerator. "Do you want some ice cream?" she asked, and opened the freezer. I shook my head no and watched her closely, too numb to say or do anything. "In fact, on second thought, I think we should celebrate tonight," and she pulled out a bottle of wine. "You don't need a jerk like him in your life... God helped you see Sean's true face... He is a liar and a cheat. I've had that uneasy feeling about him for a long time now." She poured the wine in my glass. "Everything has a purpose in life," she said. "You may not see it now but something good will come out of this... you will see."

"I don't see that at all," I finally said in a depressed voice. "What could possibly be good here?" I took the glass of wine she offered me and placed it on the coffee table.

"I know it is hard to see it now... I know it must be very painful," she said.

"I was dumped like an old rag. Where is the *good* in that? Where is the *best* in that? It was the *best dumping* I ever had!" I said, making an effort to stay composed. "First Dan and now Sean... What am I doing wrong? Why am I always being abandoned?"

"It's not about you," she rushed to correct me. "Dan didn't do it because of you... you have to get this. I've told you that you are not that powerful." She looked at me with compassion.

"You are a good friend, Marsha," I said while pacing the living room back and forth. I was not able to sit still. "I think you should take me back to my place," I finally said. I wanted to address my hurt alone.

At home I allowed myself to cry, to fall from the top as if I had been thrown off of the Empire State Building. It was a slow and painful fall. I shut my eyes and only opened them to let the tears flow. I curled up on the sofa hugging the pillow to me as if it was my lifeline. I heard the phone ringing a few times and let the answering machine pick it up. Sean's voice was clear. No hesitation. No remorse. He simply said, "Call me when you get home." I looked at the clock on the wall and saw that it was near midnight.

I didn't intend to call Sean nor did I wish to see his face. It felt like the only way I could get back at him was to remove myself from his life totally. Deep inside, however, I hoped he would put up a fight for me. I hoped he would protest and ask for my forgiveness. I hoped that he would be full of regret and sorrow.

As the night wore on, I could not help thinking about Dan... my life with him and how he had ended it. As I was grieving my loss of Sean, other earlier losses became more vivid and clear.

For the next few weeks I stayed home most of the time when I wasn't working. At first, Sean called me every day and left a message. Eventually, he stopped calling, as I never returned his calls. My pride would not permit it. In my childish anger I preferred to suffer rather than open up my heart again. I was too afraid that if I saw him, I might believe his story. I might forget. I might get hurt again. Marsha kept in close touch with me. She kept reminding me that somewhere in creation there was someone out there who was just right for me and for her... that God had our second half just waiting for the right moment to show up. But, I refused to let the future in and kept on soaking in my misfortune.

One night as I stayed home feeling sorry for myself, I tightened my grip on my pillow and let out a deep and steady cry from the center of my being. A primitive feeling of anguish stirred up in me. With a primal child's cry I sobbed and sobbed until hours had passed. I pleaded not to become invisible as the walls closed in and I tasted the bitter taste of loneliness. The empty voice of abandonment, the melancholy feeling of being cut apart and alone. Like a black hole of nothingness, my life spun around like never before. I had the sinking feeling of fading away, of wanting to disappear, of wanting to finally rest.

For a split second, in my anguish, in my agony and distress, I wished for death. For the sweet taste of silence and calm. Just for a moment, just for a brief moment, just enough to humble me, just enough for me to diffuse my anger and judgment of Dan. Did I dare to think of ending my life? I found myself thinking once more of Dan standing in his place of pain and despair. It was just enough for me to realize the anguish he must have endured for years.

I lowered my head as if he stood before me. I reached out to him as if I was reaching out to an old friend. I stood alone but not lonely anymore. Realizing what Dan must have gone through took over my entire being. It was as if I was in his body experiencing his state of mind.

Suddenly, Sean was not the center of my thoughts or my pain anymore. Knowing and understanding Dan was the core of my pain now. I had judged him so harshly for so many years and now I finally comprehended his struggle, feeling this pain of "no way out." I was able to accept him now and understand his decision.

I marveled that the pain with Sean took such a back seat. It was as if he had already served a purpose in my life by bringing me back full circle to Dan and the trauma of losing him. I felt no blame, no guilt, no anger, just a deep core acceptance of this man who had been my husband.

Everything over the past years had been colored by his death... my fears, my creativity, my relationships. And now, I felt calm and still. I knew what I had to do and I couldn't wait to begin.

CHAPTER 24

White Orchids

You must be the change you want to see in the world.
—Mahatma Gandhi

The next few days were full of realization and empowerment for me. I stopped at the travel agency and purchased a ticket to Israel. Then, I packed my suitcase and called my brother, Carmel, in Tel Aviv asking him to pick me up at the airport in two days.

"This is wonderful," he cried with excitement but quickly asked, "It's rather a short notice... is everything okay?"

"Yes, everything is fine. It is summer time... school is out and I miss you that's all."

"I can't wait," he said.

As the plane winged its way from Los Angeles to my homeland, I had many hours to contemplate my life and all that had recently occurred. The time since my separation from Sean had been the most painful yet the most vital for my emotional growth. I understood now that there was no need for self-pity or blame in this world. I finally got it that each and every one of us is in charge of our own life and that life is the total sum of the actions and decisions we make every day. We are the only ones to be held responsible for it. This very thought was most freeing.

As I sat in the quiet of the plane, I thought once more of the book I had started a few years back. Maybe this was why this story kept on insisting to be told. There was a need to break the silence for Dan's sake and for all the people who would come to kill themselves. There was a need to have completion and understanding for those who were left behind. After all, suicide is not a rare case in our society. The number of suicides is higher than the number of homicides in the U.S. Yet, we find it easier to speak about murdering and killing one another than mentioning the fact that many of us kill ourselves. Why the silence? What are we trying to hide?

I knew that Dan's method of dying was not mentioned anywhere. Not in his obituary, not at his Shiva and not on his death certificate. It was especially not mentioned in open conversations. As open as I tried to be about suicide, I found myself avoiding the topic when visiting family and friends. Making them uncomfortable didn't seem worth the effort.

Years before Dan's death a young relative of his had committed suicide. "He fell ill," I heard someone say. But his pictures were removed from the family album, his name was erased and shortly after his death he was a forgotten victim. The shame, the guilt and the blame. Above all, the fear that it might happen again. Perhaps the fear of ourselves. Do we really know ourselves well enough to say with total certainty it will not happen in our life? Is it possible that suicide might be concealed in our heart or hidden in some corner of our mind? Having recently experienced such a low point with Sean, I felt as if I had explored this hidden crevice in my own psyche and come out of it knowing what I had to do. I was glad I was flying to Tel Aviv. It felt like the next step in my growth toward health.

The next day, as we landed, I was full of energy and determination. In Tel Aviv I stayed with Mom. In her small apartment time seemed to stand still. It seemed as if I had never left. Many years had gone by since Dan's death and I noticed my mom had removed my wedding picture from the wall. In its place she had hung a photo I had sent her from L.A. in front of the old Farmer's Market. But, everything else seemed the same. The same smell of cooking from her small kitchen, the faded pillows and covers on the couch, the slightly stale smell of perfume in her bedroom. I felt comfortable in the assurance of this stability.

The morning after my arrival I rented a car and left to drive to the cemetery. I had to ask for directions at the car rental agency. The roads seemed different and many new buildings and streets had changed the view.

I stopped at a nearby flower shop and picked up the largest bouquet of orchids and gladiolus I could find. Once back in the car, I drove out of Tel Aviv for almost an hour. It was rush hour and the traffic was rather heavy. I didn't mind at all as it gave me time to reflect and to blend once again into the familiar yet new atmosphere. Tel Aviv was hot and humid, colorful and busy. I drove past the places I knew so well where Dan and I had spent time on different occasions. I thought about all those years I had spent thinking about life and love, as I traveled deeper and deeper into the land that spoke my dialogue and housed familiar characters and themes. Soon after, I entered the road leading to the cemetery and arrived at its gates.

When I parked my car, there were only two other cars beside mine. It felt so quiet and serene. The wind carried the smell of the Mediterranean Sea, cool and sweet. I walked toward the small building at the center of the entrance and knocked lightly on the door. A short, old, bearded man emerged. "Yes Madam, how can I help you?" he asked.

"I am looking for the grave site of Dan Tavor," I said, looking around his cluttered office. Old files and papers cluttered his desk.

"Give me a date... the date of death," he repeated, as I stared absently at him.

"December. It was on December ninth of 1970," I said. Then, he nodded his head and pulled off of the shelf a heavy file in book form. He turned a few pages and put his finger on Dan's name.

"Here it is... Dan Tavor... lane 87, plot 15," he said looking at me. "Do you need me to write it down for you?" he asked staring at the flowers with a smile.

"No thanks. I will remember," I replied strongly.

"Do you need a prayer book?" He reached over to hand me a small book of prayers.

"No thanks... I know what I want to say," but I smiled with gratitude.

"God bless you," he said smoothing his beard and escorting me out.

I walked down the lane slowly. On both sides there were many tombstones. Some of them had fresh flowers; some had just a few small stones to indicate a visitor had been there. Now and then I paused and read the dates, the names, the delegations of a mother, a father, a daughter, a husband… they all were here. So many different people and lives with stories to tell, just as we had them out there among the living. The scene was different for me, different than ten years earlier. I was different. My inner dialogue was different. Unlike at Dan's funeral, there was no anger in my heart, no condemnations or demands. This time I felt humbled by pain and acceptance.

I reached the grave and stood still for a long moment. Dan's tombstone was in the shape of a broken tree trunk. I had ordered it at the time, dismissing Dan's wish not to have a tombstone, thinking that I knew better. There were a few roses next to Dan's grave, perhaps a few days old. His sister I imagined. She loved red roses. Maybe she had been there with Gadi, her brother. I stood there wondering silently.

Slowly, I knelt down and put the vase at the center of the plot, cleaning around it as if I was straightening up the cold stone. I arranged the red roses, refreshing them with fresh water and placing them next to my white orchids and gladiolus. I was silent for a moment. I didn't really know what to say first. My emotions were flooding within me and it took a few minutes for me to settle down and unlock my spirit. Finally, I smiled lightly and opened up my heart.

"I miss you, Dan. Many times I think of you. It is hard out here without you. It is really hard to be left alone… just like that… I never, ever thought you would do something like you did… go like that and leave with no way of returning. Without a chance to say anything. After you left me, everyone else left me, too. All of our friends, our relatives, most of them just left. Not even a phone call. My father left me again, too. I called him before my move to the United States but he never called back. I called him a

few times but he wouldn't talk to me. I think Celina wouldn't allow him to... I don't know why Celina hated me so much. Maybe it was not Celina at all. Maybe he was just angry with me for losing you. Your father and family... they all left, too... I never heard from them again."

I cried and could not stop my tears; I cried and could not stop talking.

"I left, too. I left our home, our country... I was so very angry. I am sorry... I guess people leave when they're angry... what else is there to do? I'm not angry any more, Dan, only sad, very sad... sad for us, sad you had to leave. I am sorry if I hurt you... you left and there is no way to get you back now. I can't say much. I can't change your mind. It is all done and finished."

I stopped to breathe and looked around; there was no one in sight. Still just me and Dan and the blazing sun.

I reached out and touched Dan's tombstone, as I would reach for his shoulder in a moment of truth. *"You know, the hardest thing about being alone is that there is no one to protect my interests, no one to see that I will not be taken advantage of... because I tend to be naive like you used to say. I tend to believe, to want to believe that things are simply the way they appear to be. I need you as I needed you then. I also want to tell you this; I am really not as strong as you think. I know I appear strong and aloof sometimes, like I don't need anyone. It is only my act. I act powerful and strong in order not to feel vulnerable. It is my fear, my fear to open up and feel. But you know what the irony is? The irony is that the only one who didn't leave me in those difficult days was my mom. She stayed close to me... she cared, no matter what. I guess a mother is always a mother. She is not so bad after all. Do you remember how everyone was afraid that I would become like her? My fate is such that I am walking in her shoes now because people are talking about me just like they talked about her… like mother like daughter. So it did happen, and it is okay with me now. She is really not such a bad woman, although I must say she is childlike…very naive. I find many women to be naive like this."*

I stopped talking here as I realized that I was at peace with my mother now, too. With gratitude to Dan I embraced my mother to myself. I remained sitting on the grassy area next to Dan's tombstone all curled in; I wrapped my arms around my knees and buried my head.

"I am sorry if I hurt you, Dan. I was there with you. How could I not be part of the hurt? I was young and inexperienced. I did not understand your pain. How could I know? How could I possibly understand your hurt? I was so self-involved and self-centered… Simply selfish and naive… remember how you used to call me that?"

I had to stop here, because I was choking in my tears. They turned into an anguished cry of sorrow and regret. Of true repentance and a desire to mend our broken hearts, Dan's and mine. I remained silent and finally wiped away my tears mingled with perspiration, as the sun was burning down hard. I closed my eyes and lowered my body under the small shade of the tombstone next to Dan's grave. I found a restful spot and composed myself. The flowers were wilting under the hot rays of the sun and I realized they, too, were having a hard time.

"So, I finally have brought you your orchids, together with my gladiolus… with my truest sincerity. I wanted to tell you that I understand and love you. These flowers are a sign of my love for you. I know that I am a little late. I always seem to be late. I remember I was late at your funeral. Really, I was reluctant to show up altogether… but now, I wish for us to be in peace… I am not angry anymore, and not ashamed… I understand. I also wish for

you to forgive me… to be at peace with me."

I cleared the tears from my cheeks with my palms and closed my eyes as I was suddenly feeling tired. But, I was not ready to leave yet. I stayed for a long time. I spoke softly as one speaks to a loved one.

"You know I am writing a book about us, about you and about what you chose to do." I paused as if I was waiting to hear his reaction. *"You said once that I was a good writer… but who ever knew I would write like this about you and me… about your life and death. About your pain and sorrow. About my pain and sorrow. In many ways we are alike… only I am here and you are there. I want you to know that I understand now. I understand the pain. I remember how you used to say to me, 'You don't understand me.' So now I do. I am sorry it has taken me so long."*

I breathed deeply.

"Whoever thought that would become the purpose of my life, to hope for other people to understand as much as I have come to understand you now? There is a great deal of comfort that comes with understanding… there is a great sense of relief and peace. I know that now. It was not my place to condemn but to understand and help. I think that this will be the right thing to do… to help others understand. I know you are with me on that. Perhaps, this is our gift to each other and humanity."

I rested and did not have much more to say. It was late afternoon already and the sun was almost down. Its heat eased and gave way to the soft cool breeze from the sea. There was a tranquility and calm in the air. I noticed a few birds flying above my head in the open blue sky and I let out a sigh of relief. Finally, I felt at peace. Finally, I felt free and able to go. I stood up and smoothed my dress. Softly, I moved my hand along Dan's tombstone and let him go.

"Shalom," I whispered. *"Shalom."*

Appendix

Resources for Information about suicide,
and for Survivors after Suicide of a loved one.

The National Suicide Prevention Lifeline Number:
1-800-273-TALK (8255)
www.suicidepreventionlifeline.org

The National Hopeline Network Number:
1-800-784-2433

Substance Abuse & Mental Health Service Administration
www.samhsa.gov

Didi Hirsch Community-Mental Health Center in Los Angeles
www.suicidepreventioncenter.org
Also available Support group for
Survivors After Suicide.
SAS program Number :
310-751-5370
Crisis Line Number:
310-391-1253
4760 S. Sepulveda Blvd Culver City, Ca 90230

American Association for Suicidology
5221 Wisconsin Ave N.W., Suite 408
Washington DC 20015
202-237-2280
Fax-202-237-2282
www.suicidology.org
American Foundation for Suicide Prevention
120 Wall Street , 22 Floor

New York, NY 10005
888-333-2377
Fax-212 -363-6237
Western Division
7974 Haven Avenue, suite 250
Rancho Cucamonga, 91730
800-344-0500
Fax 909-948-0748
www.afsp.org

National Institute of Mantel Health
6001 Executive Boulevard
Bethesda, MD 20892
800-421-4211
www.nimh.nih.gov

Suicide Prevention Advocacy Network
5034 Odin's Way
Marietta , GA 30068
888-649-1366
Fax; 770-642-1419
www.spanusa.org

ABOUT THE AUTHOR

SARA SHAI is an award winning artist based in Los Angeles. She is a fomer freelance writer, a teacher and fashion designer. However, her deep-rooted passion is painting in oil and acrylic, and sculpting in marble and alabaster.

Beautiful in Black: Conversations with Suicide is her empowering personal experience and her triumph over the stigma and grief of her husband's suicide. Sara's work is poetic and lyrical. Her engagement with the material is innocent. She takes hold of her pen with the same passion that she takes hold of a brush or a chisel.

We invite you to visit www.sarashai.com , to learn more about the author's artwork, and www.BeautifulinBlack.com for books events, public appearances, CDs and tapes.

Sara Shai is available to give presentations and to speak to groups and organizations.

To book the author for your event, call 818-222-8228.

Questions and Topics for Group Discussion

1. Many say that **Beautiful in Black** is a strong woman's story. *"Sara's positive spirit and drive to excel is an inspiration of what is possible for us."* How did her story empower you?

2. On page 21 Sara says, *"I was not sure whether I cared more about mourning my loss or defending myself against the judgmental eyes."* How did the stigma and the shame associated with suicide affect her response to her husband's death? Did she cope with it effectively?

3. Viktor Frankl, in **Man's Search for Meaning**, maintains that the task of those who are left behind is to realize that something is still expected of them in their ongoing relationship with the deceased. How does this apply in this story?

4. In reacting to Dan's suicide, Sara dealt with many emotions. What were they? Did they seem appropriate in the book? How were they similar and/or different from what one might feel toward the death of someone from natural causes?

5. Each of us leaves behind a legacy when we die. What was Dan's legacy? Recall that, according to Sara, he was *"a man who desired to do the right thing."* (Page 529)

6. Has this book changed your perspective about suicide? If so, how? Do you think suicide is a choice?

7. Clarissa Estes, PhD, in her book **Women Who Run with the Wolves**, talks about the wild woman archetype. This woman relies upon her intuition, which is the treasure of a woman's psyche. When did Sara not use her intu-

ition? Would the circumstances of her life have changed if she had?

8. During Sara's younger years, women in Israel and around the world were viewed in a certain way. For many, they were seen as 'second-class citizens'. If Sara was growing up today, do you think she would have married Dan? What signals along the way might have indicated to her that this was not a good match? Do you think those signals would matter to Sara today?

9. Sara and Dan both proclaimed their love to each other. Is what the book describes genuine love? How so or how not? How does this fit in with Aunt Beth's descriptions of love? (Chapter 7)

10. How did Sara's relationship with her father influence her interaction with men?

11. Although they had similar experiences with their parents growing up, why do you think Sara and Dan reacted differently to their life situations?

12. Even though Dan was able to use his writing as a creative tool, it was not able to save him. How were Dan and Sara different with their creativity and why do you think it nurtured Sara while it did not nurture Dan?

13. Based upon what we learn about Dan in the book, do you think therapy/counseling would have prevented him from committing suicide? What would have been possible for him if he had sought help and stayed among us?

14. Where does Sara begin to mature in the book? What causes it?

15. What role does forgiveness play in Sara's life? Forgiveness of self and of others.